300 CALORIES OR LESS!

I1025710

300 CALORIES OR LESS!

ENJOY DELICIOUS RECIPES FOR JUST 300 CALORIES OR LESS

This edition published in 2013
LOVE FOOD is an imprint of Parragon Books Ltd

Parragon
Chartist House
15–17 Trim Street
Bath BA1 1HA, UK

Copyright © Parragon Books Ltd 2012

LOVE FOOD and the accompanying heart device is a registered trademark of Parragon Books Ltd in Australia, the UK, USA, India, and the EU.

www.parragon.com/lovefood

All rights reserved. No part of this publication may be reproduced, stored in a retrieval system, or transmitted, in any form or by any means, electronic, mechanical, photocopying, recording, or otherwise, without the prior permission of the copyright holder.

ISBN: 978-1-4723-1730-8

Printed in China

New recipes and introduction by Robin Donovan
New photography by Clive Streeter
Home economy for new photography by Teresa Goldfinch
Nutritional analysis by Fiona Hunter

Notes for the Reader
This book uses standard kitchen measuring spoons and cups. All spoon and cup measurements are level unless otherwise indicated. Unless otherwise stated, milk is assumed to be whole, eggs are large, individual vegetables are medium, and pepper is freshly ground black pepper. Unless otherwise stated, all root vegetables should be washed in plain water and peeled before using.

Garnishes, decorations, and serving suggestions are all optional and not necessarily included in the recipe ingredients or method. Any optional ingredients and seasoning to taste are not included in the nutritional analysis. Nutritional analysis is per serving (Serves ...) or per item (Makes ...).

The times given are only an approximate guide. Preparation times differ according to the techniques used by different people and the cooking times may also vary from those given. Optional ingredients, variations, or serving suggestions have not been included in the time calculations.

Recipes using raw or very lightly cooked eggs should be avoided by infants, the elderly, pregnant women, and people with weakened immune systems. Pregnant and breast-feeding women are advised to avoid eating peanuts and peanut products. People with nut allergies should be aware that some of the prepared ingredients used in the recipes in this book may contain nuts. Always check the packaging before use.

Vegetarians and vegans should be aware that some of the prepared ingredients used in the recipes in this book may contain animal products. Always check the package before use. If you have a wheat, gluten, or dairy allergy, please read all labels carefully and check with the manufacturer.

Contents

Introduction   6

Breakfast   22

Lunch   52

Dinner   84

Desserts & Snacks   116

Index   144

Finally, a Low-Calorie Diet Made Easy—And Delicious!

Sure, you've heard it before. Few factors have such a profound effect on our health than our weight. Achieving or maintaining a healthy weight may just be the best thing you can do for yourself. Not just for your appearance, but for every aspect of your life. You may like the way you look better, but far more important, you'll feel better, have more energy, get sick less often, be less likely to develop weight-related diseases, such as hypertension and diabetes, and you'll probably live longer, too.

While losing weight is never easy, the fact is that for most of us, it's not rocket science. Actually, it's just plain and simple arithmetic: Calories in versus calories out. Eat the same number of calories you burn to maintain weight, eat fewer than you burn to lose weight.

But, you groan, counting calories is a hassle, isn't it? It takes dedication, patience, time, and commitment. Reading every label and looking up every ingredient is so dull! Plus, there is the dreaded sense that you have to

give up all your favorite foods. If all of that makes you want to toss in the towel before you've even started, I don't blame you.

However, there is good news! Losing or maintaining your weight by sticking to a low-calorie diet doesn't have to be difficult, or even unpleasant. Choosing healthy foods— foods that are packed with nutrients instead of added fat, sugar, and other empty calories—can be just as easy as stuffing yourself with junk. And, believe it or not, it can be just as enjoyable, too. The trick is making sure that healthy, low-calorie foods are just as readily available and easy to prepare as the high-calorie foods you're accustomed to eating.

Alas, many of us are so used to grabbing convenient but unhealthy snacks on the go that we've forgotten just what a healthy diet is. Here's an easy way to remember it: fresh, whole, unprocessed fruit and veggies, lean proteins (beans, tofu, white poultry meat, fish, and even lean cuts of pork or other red meats), nuts, and whole grains are good; highly processed foods, or foods with long lists of ingredients (especially added sugars or fats), and fried foods are bad. Simple!

How to Use This Book

The book you are holding in your hands is a great resource because it provides recipes that have been developed, tested, and analyzed to make sure that the dishes they produce are not only delicious, but are also low in calories. As the title suggests, every dish in this book contains 300 calories or less.

Mix and match the recipes to come up with a complete meal plan—including breakfast, lunch, dinner, snacks, and desserts—made up of foods you love. Whether you are trying to lose weight or to simply maintain your current weight, you can easily stick to your calorie limit without having to count a thing.

For the average person trying to lose weight, nutritionists recommend a daily calorie limit of 1,200 to 1,500 calories for women and 1,500 to 2,000 calories for men. If you are hoping to simply maintain your weight, 1,800 to 2,200 calories may work

for you. Using those guidelines, you can enjoy four to six dishes from the recipes in this book each day. If you're sticking to the lower calorie limit, for instance, you can enjoy breakfast, lunch, dinner, and a snack. For the middle and higher end of the range, you might add another snack and/or a dessert (just don't forget to count any beverages, such as juice or soda, when calculating your day's totals).

Fill your larders with wholesome treats and snacks (we'll give you some ideas!) and bone up on a few quick and easy recipes, such as the ones in this book, and you may be surprised by how easy it is to stick to a healthy diet.

What *Should* You Weigh?

Right about now, you may be wondering, "Hmmm, what IS a healthy weight for me, anyway?" The best way to figure that out is to look at your Body Mass Index, or BMI, which is a fancy name for a number that refers to your weight in relation to your height.

Assuming you know how tall you are, you can calculate your BMI with a simple formula: Your weight in kilograms divided by your height in meters squared—Weight (kg)/Height (m)^2.

For instance, a 1.65-meter tall person who weighs 64 kilograms would have a BMI of 23.5, which is within the healthy range.

Here's a formula for U.S. standard measurements (weight in pounds, height in inches): Your weight in pounds divided by your height in inches squared, times by 703—Weight (lb)/Height (inches)^2 x 703.

Using standard measurements: A person who is 5 feet, 5 inches tall (65 inches) and weighs 140 pounds would have a BMI of 23.3:

$140/65^2 \times 703 = 23.3$ or ...

$65 \times 65 = 4{,}225$; $140 \div 4{,}225 = 0.033136$; $0.033136 \times 703 = 23.3$ (rounded off)

A healthy weight person will have a BMI between 18.5 and 24.9. If you are within this range, congratulations! While you may want to adopt healthier eating habits, you don't have a weight problem, so you don't need to worry about losing weight. If, however, your BMI is 25 or higher, you can use this book to overhaul your diet and achieve a healthier weight.

Setting a goal weight can be tricky. There is a temptation to shoot for the moon, so to speak, and set a goal that would put your BMI at a svelte 18.5, but if you're starting out, say, in the high 20s, be careful about setting yourself up for disappointment and failure. Try setting an easier goal to start. For instance, you might set a goal that would bring your BMI down to 27. Once you've achieved that weight and maintained it for a while, you can reevaluate and, with that success under your belt, set a new goal that brings your BMI down to, say, 24.

Further, if your goal is to lose weight, don't try to lose it too fast. You'll have longer lasting success if you lose around two pounds per week. While fad diets and starvation may help you shed pounds fast, chances are you'll gain the weight back the minute you go back to eating normally. Far better is a diet plan that helps you develop healthier habits that you can maintain for the long haul. This book will help you learn how to choose healthier alternatives for many of your favorite foods. Stick with it for a month or two, and you'll likely find that you begin to prefer the healthier options because they leave you feeling better, more energetic, less sluggish, and, well, healthier.

And rest assured, no one is expecting you to be a saint. Go ahead and cheat every once in a while. If you find your mother's cheesecake simply irresistible, go ahead and indulge in a slice (or two!) the next time you visit. If buttered popcorn brings you incomparable joy when you go to the movies, let yourself live a little now and then. What's more important is that you make healthy choices in your everyday life. Keeping your cupboards stocked with wholesome, nutritious foods and learning to prepare healthy meals will give you

the tools you need to achieve or maintain a healthy weight.

If your goal is to lose weight, plan to eat around 1,200 to 1,500 calories per day for women or 1,500 to 2,000 calories for men. If your goal is to maintain your weight, 1,800 to 2,200 calories per day should be fine. This book makes that easy because every recipe in it contains 300 calories or less per serving, making it simple to mix and match for a balanced diet that is within your allowed calorie range. For instance, you might choose one breakfast dish, one lunch dish, one dinner dish, a snack, and, if you're feeling indulgent, a dessert. But don't let the categories limit you. There's nothing wrong with having breakfast for dinner or dinner for lunch! The most important thing is eating a range of nutritious foods (and sorry, eating five desserts every day is not okay, even if it would be within the calorie limits!).

Watch Your Portions

In addition to choosing healthy foods, it's important to pay attention to portion sizes. A small bowl of pasta is perfectly acceptable, but keep an eye on the amount you are giving yourself:

- A 3-ounce serving of meat is about the size of a deck of cards
- A 6-ounce serving of white fish is about the size of a checkbook
- A 3-ounce serving of sliced lunchmeat is about the size of 3 CDs
- A 1-ounce serving of cheese is the size of a pair of dice
- 1 cup of potatoes, rice, or cereal is about the size of a baseball
- ½ cup of ice cream or frozen yogurt is about the size of 2 golf balls
- 1 cup of fruit is about the size of a small fist

Mindful Eating

One of the best practices to help keep you on track is just to pay attention when you are eating. Instead of watching television or checking your e-mails while you eat, really focus on your food—and you'll not only likely eat less but you'll enjoy your food more.

It takes about 20 minutes for your brain to get a message from your stomach saying it is satisfied. As a result, eating slowly will also help to prevent overeating by giving your stomach a chance to send the message to your brain that it has had enough before you overindulge.

Keeping a Food Diary

If you have a tendency to eat mindlessly or simply eat the foods and quantities you do out of habit, a food diary will be an extremely useful tool. By learning to pay attention to every morsel of food that passes your lips, you'll learn a lot about when, why, and what you eat.

You'll probably be surprised by some of the things you learn. Just by increasing your awareness of your eating habits, you'll find changing them to be much easier. Perhaps you don't even realize that you always put a double serving of cream cheese on your morning bagel or eat half the bag of chips that supposedly contains five servings.

Take your food diary with you wherever you go and use it to record every single thing you eat. Do this for at least a full week, or ideally a month.

To make your food diary as useful as possible, include details about what, when, and how much you eat. For instance, "6 p.m.: 3 slices of veggie pizza with extra cheese in the car on the way home" is a more useful entry than simply "pizza." To really make the diary useful, consider including other details, such as what you were doing while you ate (watching television, reading, driving, chatting with a friend), as well as how you were feeling (sad, happy, stressed out) at the time.

All of this information will help you identify the times that you are likely to overeat or any emotional cues that trigger poor eating habits. It will also help you to compensate for indulgences. For instance, if you eat a bacon cheeseburger for lunch one day, you can make up for it by having a salad with low-fat dressing the next.

Keeping track of the times you eat, too, can help you to regulate your appetite. Eating meals and snacks at regular intervals throughout the day will keep you from ever becoming ravenous—a sure setup for bingeing on unhealthy foods.

What is a Healthy Diet?

How much and how often you eat are important but, of course, you can't overlook the significance of what you eat. Specifically, a healthy diet includes a lot of fresh fruit and vegetables; lean proteins, such as beans, tofu, fish, and shellfish, skinless white poultry meat, and nuts; and whole grains, such as brown rice, whole-wheat breads, and quinoa.

A healthy plate looks something like this:

Fill half of your plate with fresh vegetables and fruit, one-quarter with whole grains, such as brown rice or quinoa, and the other quarter with lean protein, such as fish, beans, tofu, or skinless chicken breast.

It's About What You Can Eat, Not What You Can't

Instead of thinking of a healthy diet as one of deprivation, think instead of all the delicious and wholesome foods you can eat. In fact, the more variety in your diet the better, because this helps to ensure that you get all of the necessary nutrients, including vitamins, minerals, fiber, protein, healthy fats, and complex carbohydrates. Eating a range of foods also limits your risk of overexposure to certain toxic chemicals, such as pesticides, that may be present in certain foods.

Eating a rainbow of fruit and vegetables—orange citrus and melon, yellow pineapple, green apples, red bell peppers and tomatoes, purple eggplant, and blueberries, for instance—keeps your meals interesting and also provides you with a wide range of vitamins and other nutrients.

High-fiber foods, including fresh fruits, vegetables, beans, and whole grains, are packed with nutrients and are relatively low in calories, making them great candidates for satisfying hunger. Fiber also keeps you feeling fuller for longer, so you won't be tempted to overeat between meals.

Why Whole Grains?

Whole grains are unrefined grains that contain the entire grain kernel. Refined grains, on the other hand, have been milled to remove the bran and germ, giving them a more palatable texture but also stripping them of vital nutrients, such as iron, fiber, and the B vitamins. In a healthy diet, at least half of the grains or grain products consumed should be whole grains.

Healthy Fats

Healthy fats, also known as monounsaturated fats, such as those from canola oil or olive oil, avocadoes, and nuts, provide important nutrients and help with the absorption of many vitamins. These fats are a crucial part of a healthy diet. Solid fats, such as butter, lard and other animal fat, shortening, stick margarine, and hydrogenated vegetable oils are high in saturated fat, cholesterol, and trans fat and should be avoided as much as possible.

Read the Fine Print!

In order to maintain a healthy diet while juggling our fast-paced lives, many of us have no choice but to rely on prepared or convenience foods. Don't worry, however—those foods aren't off-limits. In fact, these days, the prepared foods aisle in the supermarket has a lot of healthy options. You just need to know how to recognize them. That's where reading nutrition labels comes in. These labels contain copious information, including how many calories are in each serving of the food and, equally important, how many servings are in the package. You'll also find valuable information about the food's cholesterol, fat, protein, fiber, and sodium content. See below for a breakdown of daily requirements.

Calories and other values	Grams/day for 1,500-calorie diet	Grams/day for 1,200-calorie diet
30–35% of cal. from fat*	50–60g	40–45g
15–20% of cal. from protein	45–60g	35–50g
45–65% of cal. from carbs	135–195g	110–155g
Fiber	25g	20g
Sodium	<2,300mg	<2,300mg
Cholesterol	<300mg	<300mg

* The majority of the fat in your diet, 20 to 25 percent of total calories, should be unsaturated with the remaining 10 to 15 percent saturated. Trans fats should be avoided.

Get Moving!

Wouldn't it be great if we could all look and feel fantastic without any work? Well, dream on! Looking and feeling your best requires effort. Not only do you have to make good food choices, but you'll also need to participate in regular physical activity.

But wait—before you get your panties in a bunch, take comfort in the fact that you don't have to devote hours of each day to sweating it out at the gym. In fact, just adding a few 10-minute bursts of activity throughout your day may be enough to rev your metabolism so you'll burn more calories, lose weight, and, better yet, look and feel your best.

Walking is one of the easiest ways to work more activity into your day-to-day routines. You can start out by simply walking around the block at a brisk pace at lunchtime, or even parking a couple of blocks from work instead of right in front. Take the stairs instead of the elevator, walk to do your errands instead of driving, or grab a coworker for a lunchtime stroll (and gossip session!).

Other daily activities can serve as exercise, too. Even chores, such as housekeeping and gardening, will get your blood pumping if you approach them with enthusiasm.

People who are very social often enjoy participating in exercise classes, dance lessons, or sports leagues. If you're a person who likes taking risks or are a nature lover, rock climbing, hiking, or mountain biking may be just your cup of joe. Walking, running, and yoga are good options for people who crave time to be alone with their thoughts.

The following chart shows the per hour calories burned for a wide range of activities.

Physical Activity	Calories/Hour*
Stretching	180
Weight lifting (light workout)	220
Walking (3½ mph)	280
Bicycling (<10 mph)	290
Light gardening/yard work	330
Dancing	330
Golf (walking and carrying clubs)	330
Hiking	370
Heavy yard work (chopping wood)	440
Weight lifting (vigorous effort)	440
Basketball (vigorous)	440
Walking (4½ mph)	460
Aerobics	480
Swimming (slow freestyle laps)	510
Running/jogging (5 mph)	590
Bicycling (>10 mph)	590

*Calories per hour for 154-pound person

No time for exercise? Try working these activities into your day:

• Walk or bike to work, to school, or to the store instead of driving
• Park your car or get off the bus a few blocks from your destination
• Take the stairs instead of the elevator
• Spend 10 minutes stretching at your desk
• Walk around the block instead of hanging out in the breakroom at work
• Play a game of tag with your kids before dinner
• Take your dog to a neighborhood park for a game of fetch
• Mow the lawn, rake the leaves, or do some weeding in the yard when you get home

• Use hand weights or an exercise band, or do sit-ups or push-ups while you watch television

Once you find an activity you enjoy, make a commitment to do it regularly (3 to 5 times per week) for a minimum of 30 days. By the end of that time, it's more than likely that your new routine will have become such a habit that you won't be able to imagine giving it up.

How Much Exercise Do You Need?

Ideally, every single one of us should be participating in a minimum of 30 to 60 minutes of moderate to intense physical activity every day, but while a lot is better than a little, a little is certainly better than none. Start out doing as much as you can each day and then increase the amount of time by a few minutes each day.

Shopping for a Healthy Diet

When trying to stick to a healthy diet, the supermarket can be a minefield, full of enticing—and off-limits—treats that are like ticking time bombs, poised to blow all of your good intentions out of the water.

Fresh foods are usually found around the perimeter of the store, so try to stick to these areas as much as possible, loading your cart with fresh fruits, veggies, lean proteins, and the like. Duck into the center aisles only when needed, say, for a loaf of whole-grain sandwich bread, some guilt-free condiments, such as mustard and vinegar, or the occasional healthy treat, such as low-fat frozen yogurt.

Stock up on snack foods and other quick-grab, easy-to-prepare items that are packed with nutrition instead of fat, sugar, or calories. These include fresh fruit and veggies as well as whole-grain crackers, low-fat dairy products, nuts and seeds, and dried fruits.

Grab-and-Go Healthy Snack Foods

- Fresh fruit (apples, berries, oranges, pineapple, bananas)
- Fresh vegetables (especially baby carrots, celery, bell peppers, cherry tomatoes, and other veggies that can be eaten raw with minimal prep)

- Dried fruit
- Nuts
- Whole-grain crackers
- Low-fat dairy products (yogurt, skim milk, reduced-fat cheeses)
- Whole-grain or high-fiber, low-sugar cereals

- Sweet treats (candy, cookies, ice cream)
- Soda and juice

Standby Staples for Quick-and-Easy Meals

- Whole-wheat pasta
- Brown rice
- Quinoa
- Canned beans (black, garbanzo/chickpea, pinto)
- Winter greens (chard, kale, mustard greens)
- Salad greens (lettuce, baby spinach, arugula)
- Summer or winter squashes (zucchini, crook neck, patty pan, butternut, acorn)
- Sweet potatoes or yams
- Tofu
- Skinless chicken breasts
- Pork tenderloin
- Fish or shellfish

Foods to Steer Your Cart Clear Of

- Whole-fat dairy products
- Fatty meats
- White breads
- White rice
- High-sugar cereals

Tips for Easy, Healthy Cooking

Cooking for yourself is the best way to be sure that the food you eat is full of beneficial nutrients and light on fat and empty calories. Here are a few tips to take into the kitchen. Follow them to lighten up your dishes without losing the taste factor.

Add Flavor Without Adding Calories

Dishes don't have to be high in calories to be delicious. Instead of adding flavor by using high-fat options, such as butter or cheese, choose healthier, low-fat ingredients, such as the ones listed below, that add plenty of flavor without the calories.

- Aromatics such as garlic, onions, and fresh ginger
- Mustard
- Horseradish
- Citrus juice and zest
- Hot sauce or salsa
- Fresh, dried, or pickled chiles
- Capers
- Pickles, pickled vegetables, or pickle relish
- Dried spices (cayenne, chili powder, cumin, cinnamon, etc.)
- Fresh or dried herbs (thyme, oregano, basil, rosemary, dill, etc.)

- Vinegar (wine, balsamic, or flavored with herbs or fruit)

Choose Your Cooking Fat Wisely

One of the easiest ways to cut calories and saturated fat from your home cooking is to reduce the amount and/or change the type of fat that you use to cook. Many recipes will call for, say, 2 tablespoons of butter when just a little splash of vegetable oil would do the job just as well. Not only are you using less of the fat this way, but, unlike butter, vegetable oil contains less saturated fat or cholesterol.

Get yourself a can of olive, canola, or other vegetable oil spray and use it to coat your skillets with a thin film of heart-healthy oil whenever a recipe calls for sautéing in oil. This spray can also be used to coat baking pans for baking or to coat vegetables for roasting.

Choose Your Cooking Method Wisely

We all know that veggies are good for us, but you can override nearly all of a vegetable's health benefits by choosing the wrong cooking method. For instance, zucchini is low in calories but high in a host of beneficial nutrients, including vitamin C and potassium. Dunk zucchini in batter and deep-fry it and suddenly it's just a fat-and-calorie bomb. Steaming, roasting, and light sautéing are far better options for cooking vegetables.

The Sweet Stuff

Refined sugar provides empty calories. In other words, all you get for those calories are extra pounds without any extra nutrients. Fruit and fruit juices are great substitutes because they provide sweetness to dishes with fewer added calories and more additional nutrients. Fruit and fruit purees, such as applesauce, can be used in both savory and sweet sauces, as well as in baked goods. Try replacing half of the sugar in your favorite cake or muffin recipe with applesauce and you will find that the result is even more moist and delicious than the regular way.

Sample One-Week Meal Plan

Monday:
Breakfast: Apple Spice Oatmeal
Lunch: Chicken & Spicy Peanut Salad
Dinner: Spaghetti with Bacon-Tomato Sauce
Snack/Dessert: Caramel Popcorn Bites

Tuesday:
Breakfast: Cherry Almond Granola
Lunch: Falafel Pita Pockets
Dinner: White Chicken Chili
Snack/Dessert: Pear & Blueberry Strudel

Wednesday:
Breakfast: Berry Rhubarb Muffins
Lunch: Shrimp Taco Salad
Dinner: Spicy Corn Chowder
Snack/Dessert: Buttermilk Brownies

Thursday:
Breakfast: Berry Sunrise Smoothie
Lunch: Turkey-Avocado & BLT Wrap
Dinner: Chicken & Vegetable Enchiladas
Snack/Dessert: Maple-Nut Granola Bars

Friday:
Breakfast: Crustless Corn & Cheddar Quiche
Lunch: Tomato & Feta Salad
Dinner: Shrimp & Sausage Jambalaya
Snack/Dessert: Apple-Berry Crisp

Saturday:
Breakfast: Pumpkin Pecan Pancakes
Lunch: Crab Salad Sandwiches
Dinner: Broccoli Pizza
Snack/Dessert: Chocolate Soufflés

Sunday:
Breakfast: Poached Eggs in Tomato Sauce
Lunch: Roasted Vegetable Melts
Dinner: Halibut with Romesco Sauce
Snack/Dessert: Mini Pumpkin Cheesecakes

Chapter 1
Breakfast

apple spice oatmeal

Vegetarian

Calories: 300   **Fat:** 8g   **Sat. Fat:** 3g   **Salt:** 0.7g   **Carb.:** 27.5g
Cook: 25 min.   **Prep:** 10 min.

Serves 6

2 sprays of vegetable oil spray

2 large eggs

⅓ cup skim milk

½ cup firmly packed light brown sugar

¼ cup applesauce

1 teaspoon baking powder

½ teaspoon salt

½ teaspoon ground cinnamon

2 cups rolled oats

2 large, red-skinned apples, cored and diced

½ cup dried fruit (raisins, apricots, cranberries, cherries, or a combination)

1 tablespoon unsalted butter, melted

1 Preheat the oven to 375° F. Coat a shallow, wide ovenproof dish or six 1-cup ramekins (individual ceramic dishes) with vegetable oil spray.

2 Beat the eggs and milk in a bowl. Add the brown sugar, applesauce, baking powder, salt, and cinnamon and stir until thoroughly mixed. Stir in the oats, apples, and dried fruit and mix well.

3 Spoon the mixture into the prepared ovenproof dish (or ramekins), add dabs of the butter, and bake in the preheated oven for about 25 minutes, or until hot and bubbling.

cherry almond granola

Vegan

Calories: 242   **Fat:** 11g   **Sat. Fat:** 3.5g   **Salt:** 0.1g   **Carb.:** 16g
Cook: 1¼ hr.   **Prep:** 15 min.

Serves 10

1 spray of vegetable oil spray

2½ cups rolled oats

½ cup shredded, unsweetened dried coconut

¼ cup slivered almonds

¼ cup ground flaxseed

½ teaspoon salt

½ cup maple syrup

½ cup water

1 tablespoon vegetable oil

1 teaspoon vanilla extract

½ cup pitted dried cherries, chopped

1 Preheat the oven to 275°F. Line a large baking sheet with parchment paper and spray it lightly with the vegetable oil spray.

2 In a large bowl, combine the oats, coconut, almonds, flaxseed, and salt and stir to mix well. In a small bowl, combine the maple syrup, water, vegetable oil, and vanilla extract. Pour the liquid mixture over the dry mixture and stir well. Pour the mixture onto the prepared baking sheet and spread out into an even layer.

3 Bake in the preheated oven for about 45 minutes, then stir well and spread out again into an even layer. Continue to bake for about another 30–40 minutes, until crisp and beginning to brown. Stir in the cherries and let cool to room temperature.

4 Store in a tightly covered container at room temperature for up to a week.

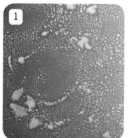

blueberry & honey yogurt

 Vegetarian

 Quick & Easy

Calories: 215   **Fat:** 11g   **Sat. Fat:** 2g   **Salt:** Trace   **Carb.:** 18g
Cook: 5 min.   **Prep:** 15 min.

Serves 4

3 tablespoons honey

¾ cup mixed unsalted nuts

½ cup reduced-fat Greek-style yogurt

1½ cups fresh blueberries

1 Heat the honey in a small saucepan over medium heat. Add the nuts and stir until they are well coated. Remove from the heat and let cool slightly.

2 Divide the yogurt among four serving bowls, then spoon the nut mixture over the yogurt, add the blueberries among the bowls, and serve immediately.

berry rhubarb muffins

Calories: 300 **Fat:** 9.5g **Sat. Fat:** 4g **Salt:** 0.7g **Carb.:** 52g
Cook: 20–25 min. **Prep:** 15 min. plus cooling

Makes 12

1 spray of vegetable oil spray

1¼ cups all-purpose flour

1 cup whole-wheat flour

½ cup ground flaxseed

1 teaspoon baking powder

1 teaspoon baking soda

4 tablespoons unsalted butter, softened

1 cup sugar

½ cup light brown sugar

1 cup low-fat buttermilk

1 large egg

1 teaspoon vanilla extract

1 cup finely diced rhubarb (fresh or frozen)

1 cup diced strawberries (fresh or frozen)

salt

Crumb topping

1 tablespoon unsalted butter

2 tablespoons all-purpose flour

2 tablespoons packed light brown sugar

2 teaspoons ground flaxseed

2 tablespoons pecan pieces

1 Preheat the oven to 400°F. Spray a 12-cup muffin pan with vegetable oil spray.

2 To make the muffin batter, combine the flours, flaxseed, baking powder, baking soda, and ⅛ teaspoon of salt in a medium bowl and stir well. In a large bowl, cream together the butter and sugars with an electric mixer. Add the buttermilk, egg, and vanilla extract to the butter-sugar mixture and beat on medium–high speed until well combined. Add the flour mixture in three batches, beating on medium speed after each addition until just incorporated. Fold in the rhubarb and strawberries with a rubber spatula until well mixed.

3 Spoon the batter into the prepared muffin pan, dividing it equally among the 12 cups.

4 To make the topping, combine the butter, flour, brown sugar, flaxseed, and a pinch of salt in a food processor and process until the mixture has the texture of coarse bread crumbs. Add the pecans and pulse a few times until the pecans are chopped small. Sprinkle the topping evenly over the muffin batter.

5 Bake in the preheated oven for 20–25 minutes, or until lightly browned on top and a toothpick inserted into the center comes out clean. Remove from the oven and cool in the pan on a wire rack for about 15 minutes, then remove the muffins from the pan. Serve warm or at room temperature.

berry sunrise smoothie

Stay Fuller For Longer | Wheat, Gluten & Dairy Free | Quick & Easy | Vegan

Calories: 259   **Fat:** 4g   **Sat. Fat:** 0.7g   **Salt:** Trace   **Carb.:** 48g
Cook: No cooking   **Prep:** 5 min.

Serves 1

1 banana

2 ounces silken tofu, drained

¾ cup orange juice

1 cup frozen mixed berries

1 Coarsely chop the banana and the tofu into smaller pieces.

2 Place all of the ingredients in a blender on high speed and then process until smooth. Let the smoothie settle for a few seconds and then process again to fully blend.

3 Serve the smoothie immediately in a tall drinking glass.

pumpkin pecan pancakes

Quick & Easy

Vegetarian

Calories: 228   **Fat:** 4.5g   **Sat. Fat:** 0.8g   **Salt:** 0.6g   **Carb.:** 43.7g
Cook: 10 min.   **Prep:** 5 min.

Serves 6

1 cup flour

½ cup chopped pecans

¼ cup firmly packed light brown sugar

2 teaspoons baking powder

½ teaspoon cinnamon

¼ teaspoon salt

1 large egg

1½ cups low-fat buttermilk

½ cup pumpkin puree

1 teaspoon vanilla extract

1 spray of vegetable oil spray

½ cup maple syrup, to serve

1 In a medium bowl, combine the flour, pecans, brown sugar, baking powder, cinnamon, and salt. In a large bowl, whisk the egg, buttermilk, pumpkin puree, and vanilla extract. Whisk the dry ingredients into the wet ingredients and mix well.

2 Spray a nonstick skillet with the vegetable oil spray and heat over medium–high heat. When hot, ladle in the batter ¼ cup at a time to make 3–4-inch pancakes.

3 Cook for about 2–3 minutes, or until bubbles begin to burst in the top and the bottom is lightly browned. Flip over and cook for about another 2 minutes, or until the second side is lightly browned. Serve immediately with maple syrup.

chocolate banana smoothie

Stay Fuller For Longer   Wheat, Gluten & Dairy Free   Vegetarian   Quick & Easy

Calories: 271   **Fat:** 9g   **Sat. Fat:** 2.5g   **Salt:** 0.3g   **Carb.:** 33.5g

Cook: No cooking   **Prep:** 5 min.

Serves 1

½ banana

2 ounces silken tofu, drained

¾ cup low-fat soy milk

1 tablespoon honey

2 tablespoons unsweetened cocoa powder

¼ teaspoon vanilla extract

1 Coarsely chop the banana and the tofu into smaller pieces.

2 Combine all of the ingredients in a blender on high speed until well mixed and the cocoa powder has been fully incorporated.

3 Serve the smoothie immediately in a tall drinking glass.

whole-wheat crepes

Stay Fuller For Longer

Vegetarian

Calories: 238   **Fat:** 13g   **Sat. Fat:** 6g   **Salt:** 0.8g   **Carb.:** 38g
Cook: 20–30 min.   **Prep:** 10 min.

Serves 6

Mushroom filling

1 tablespoon olive oil

1 garlic clove, finely chopped

1 shallot, finely chopped

1¼ pounds white button mushrooms, sliced

½ teaspoon salt

½ teaspoon pepper

Crepes

1 cup whole-wheat flour

2 large eggs

1¼ cups skim milk

¼ teaspoon salt

2 tablespoons unsalted butter, melted

2 sprays of vegetable oil spray

½ cup low-fat sour cream, to serve

3 tablespoons finely chopped chives, to garnish

1 To make the mushroom filling, heat the oil in a large skillet over medium–high heat. Add the garlic and shallot and cook for about 5 minutes, stirring occasionally, until soft. Add the mushrooms and continue to cook for about 5 minutes, stirring, until they soften and begin to brown. Season with the salt and pepper. Remove from heat and set aside.

2 To make the crepes, place the flour, eggs, milk, salt, and butter in a medium bowl. Beat together with an electric mixer.

3 Coat a large nonstick skillet with vegetable oil spray and place it over medium heat. When the skillet is hot, ladle the batter, about a ¼ cup at a time, into the hot skillet. Tilt the skillet this way and that to spread the batter into a thin, even circle about 6 inches in diameter. Cook for about 1 minute, until the crepe begins to brown lightly on the bottom. Using a spatula, gently flip the crepe over and cook for another 45 seconds on the other side, or until it is lightly browned. Stack the crepes as they are cooked and keep warm.

4 When all of the crepes are cooked, spoon 2–3 tablespoons of the filling onto each crepe and fold in half twice. Serve with a dollop of sour cream and garnish with finely chopped chives.

breakfast burrito

Vegetarian

Quick & Easy

Calories: 288   **Fat:** 6g   **Sat. Fat:** 2.5g   **Salt:** 2.8g   **Carb.:** 47g
Cook: 5 min.   **Prep:** 5 min.

Serves 1

¼ cup egg substitute (or 2 egg whites)

pinch of salt

¼ teaspoon pepper

1 scallion, thinly sliced

1 spray of vegetable oil spray

¼ cup diced red or green bell pepper

2 tablespoons canned black beans, rinsed

1 whole-wheat flour tortilla, warmed

2 tablespoons crumbled vegetarian feta cheese

2 tablespoons salsa

1 teaspoon finely chopped cilantro

1 In a small bowl, combine the egg substitute, salt, pepper, and scallion and stir well.

2 Spray a nonstick skillet with vegetable oil spray and place it over medium–high heat. Add the bell pepper and cook, stirring, for about 3 minutes, or until it begins to soften. Reduce the heat to medium, pour in the egg mixture, and cook, stirring often, for another 1–2 minutes, or until the egg sets.

3 Put the beans in a microwave-safe bowl and microwave on high for about 1 minute, or until heated through.

4 Spoon the cooked egg mixture onto the tortilla. Top with the beans, cheese, salsa, and cilantro. Serve immediately.

crustless corn & cheddar quiche

Calories: 298 **Fat:** 19g **Sat. Fat:** 10g **Salt:** 1.8g **Carb.:** 14g
Cook: 35–40 min. **Prep:** 15 min.

Serves 6

1 spray of vegetable oil spray

2 tablespoons dried bread crumbs

2 teaspoons unsalted butter

½ onion, diced

1 garlic clove, finely chopped

4 large eggs

2 cups skim milk

3 scallions, thinly sliced

1 tablespoon all-purpose flour

1 teaspoon salt

½ teaspoon pepper

dash of hot pepper sauce, or to taste

1 cup frozen corn kernels, thawed

1¾ cups shredded sharp cheddar cheese

1 Preheat the oven to 425°F. Spray a 9-inch pie dish with the oil and coat with the bread crumbs.

2 Melt the butter in a heavy skillet over medium–high heat. Add the onion and garlic and cook, stirring, for about 5 minutes, or until soft. Remove from the heat.

3 In a large bowl, whisk the eggs, milk, scallions, flour, salt, pepper, and hot pepper sauce. Stir in the corn, sautéed onions and garlic, and three-quarters of the cheese. Pour the mixture into the prepared pie dish and sprinkle the remaining cheese evenly over the top.

4 Bake in the preheated oven for about 35–40 minutes, or until the top is golden brown and the quiche is set in the center. Remove from oven and set on a rack to cool. Cut into wedges and serve warm or at room temperature.

egg white omelet

Vegetarian

Quick & Easy

Calories: 160   **Fat:** 10g   **Sat. Fat:** 6g   **Salt:** 0.8g   **Carb.:** 4g
Cook: 3–5 min.   **Prep:** 15 min.

Serves 1

¼ red bell pepper, seeded

½ cup egg substitute or 2 egg whites

1 scallion, thinly sliced

pinch of salt

pinch of pepper

1 spray of vegetable or olive oil spray

1 ounce fresh vegetarian goat cheese

2 teaspoons chopped fresh basil

1 Preheat the broiler. Put the bell pepper on a baking sheet under the broiler, skin side up, and roast until it begins to blacken. Remove and place in a plastic bag or a bowl covered with plastic wrap and set aside until cool enough to handle. Discard the blackened skin and dice the pepper.

2 In a small bowl, mix the egg substitute or egg whites, scallion, salt, and pepper, stirring to combine well.

3 Coat a skillet with the vegetable or olive oil spray and heat over medium heat. Add the egg mixture and cook for about 3 minutes, or until the egg is set, turning the skillet frequently and running a spatula around the edge to maintain a thin, even layer of egg.

4 Crumble the goat cheese in a strip down the center of the omelet, then top with the diced bell pepper and the basil. Fold the sides over the filing and slide the omelet onto a plate. Serve immediately.

poached eggs in tomato sauce

Vegetarian

Calories: 299   **Fat:** 16g   **Sat. Fat:** 5g   **Salt:** 1.6g   **Carb.:** 21g
Cook: 30–35 min.   **Prep:** 10 min.

Serves 4

1 tablespoon olive oil

1 small onion, diced

2 garlic cloves, finely chopped

¼ teaspoon salt

½ teaspoon pepper

¼ teaspoon crushed red pepper flakes

¼ cup vegetarian red wine

1 (14½-ounce) can diced tomatoes, with juice

2 teaspoons finely chopped fresh oregano, thyme, basil, sage, or other fresh herb

4 large eggs

4 slices toasted whole-wheat sourdough bread, to serve

2 tablespoons finely chopped Kalamata olives, to serve

⅓ cup grated vegetarian Parmesan-style cheese, to serve

1 Heat the oil in a large skillet over medium–high heat. Add the onion and garlic and cook, stirring occasionally, for about 5 minutes, or until soft. Add the salt, pepper, red pepper flakes, and wine and cook for another few minutes, until the liquid has mostly evaporated. Add the tomatoes and their juice, bring to a boil, then reduce the heat to medium–low and simmer for about 15–20 minutes, or until the sauce thickens. Stir in the fresh herbs.

2 Make four wells in the sauce and carefully crack the eggs into them. Cover and cook at a hearty simmer for about 7–9 minutes, or until the whites are set but the yolks are still runny.

3 Put the toast slices on four serving plates. Carefully scoop the eggs out of the sauce and place one on each slice of toast. Place spoonfuls of the sauce around the egg and top with a sprinkling of chopped olives and Parmesan-style cheese. Serve immediately.

cheesy corn muffins

Vegetarian

Calories: 300   **Fat:** 13g   **Sat. Fat:** 7g   **Salt:** 0.9g   **Carb.:** 39g
Cook: 30 min.   **Prep:** 10 min.

Makes 12

2 sprays of vegetable oil spray

1 cup all-purpose flour

1 cup yellow cornmeal

¾ cup sugar

2 teaspoons baking powder

1 teaspoon salt

2 large eggs

1 cup skim milk

1 cup fresh or frozen corn

¾ cup chopped mild green or jalapeno chiles

6 tablespoons unsalted butter, melted

1¼ cups grated vegetarian cheddar cheese

1 Preheat the oven to 350°F. Spray a 12-cup muffin pan with vegetable oil spray.

2 In a large mixing bowl, combine the flour, cornmeal, sugar, baking powder, and salt. In a medium bowl, beat together the eggs, milk, corn, chiles, butter, and half the cheese. Add the wet ingredients to the dry ingredients and mix well.

3 Divide the batter evenly between the muffin cups and sprinkle with the remaining cheese. Bake in the preheated oven for about 30 minutes, or until lightly browned on top and a toothpick inserted into the center of one of the muffins comes out clean. Serve warm or at room temperature.

ham & cheese scones

Calories: 265   **Fat:** 12g   **Sat. Fat:** 7g   **Salt:** 1.4g   **Carb.:** 31g
Cook: 25 min.   **Prep:** 10 min.

Makes 8

2 ¼ cups all-purpose flour, plus extra for dusting

2 teaspoons baking powder

1 teaspoon sugar

½ teaspoon baking soda

½ teaspoon salt

pinch of pepper

4 tablespoons unsalted butter, cut into small pieces

1 ¼ cups low-fat buttermilk

1 cup shredded cheddar cheese

4 ounces cooked ham, diced

3 scallions, thinly sliced

1 Preheat the oven to 400°F. Line a baking sheet with parchment paper.

2 In a large bowl, combine the flour, baking powder, sugar, baking soda, salt, and pepper. Add the butter and rub the mixture between your hands or cut it in with a pastry cutter until the texture resembles coarse bread crumbs. This can also be achieved by pulsing the dry ingredients with the butter in a food processor.

3 Add the buttermilk, cheese, ham, and scallions and stir to mix well. The dough will be fairly sticky. On a lightly floured board, knead the dough several times with floured hands.

4 Transfer the dough to the prepared baking sheet and pat it out into a circle about ½-inch thick and about 9 inches in diameter. Score into wedges with a sharp knife or pizza cutter.

5 Bake in the preheated oven for about 25 minutes, or until golden brown. Cool on a wire rack. Serve the scones warm or at room temperature.

Chapter 2

Lunch

chicken cobb salad

Quick & Easy

Calories: 300   **Fat:** 18g   **Sat. Fat:** 6g   **Salt:** 1.3g   **Carb.:** 6.5g
Cook: 15 min.   **Prep:** 10 min.

Serves 4

Dressing

2 tablespoons balsamic vinegar

1 teaspoon Dijon mustard

2 tablespoons olive oil

½ teaspoon salt

¼ teaspoon pepper

Salad

2 eggs

1 spray of vegetable oil spray

4 strips turkey bacon

6 cups chopped romaine lettuce

2 tomatoes, cut into wedges

1⅓ cups diced, cooked skinless, boneless
chicken breast

½ cup crumbled blue cheese

1 Whisk all the dressing ingredients in a small bowl until emulsified.

2 Bring a small saucepan of water to a boil. Add the eggs and simmer for about 13 minutes, until hard boiled. Remove, put the eggs into ice water, and set aside until cool. Peel the eggs, discard the yolks, and chop the whites.

3 Spray a nonstick skillet with vegetable oil and heat it over medium–high heat. Add the turkey bacon and cook for about 2–3 minutes per side, or until lightly browned and crisp.

4 In a large bowl, combine the lettuce and tomato and toss to mix. Add several spoonfuls of the dressing and toss again to coat. Divide the salad equally among four serving plates. Top each with the chicken, turkey bacon, cheese, and chopped egg white. Drizzle with the remaining dressing and serve immediately.

tomato & feta salad

Vegetarian

Quick & Easy

Calories: 265   **Fat:** 17g   **Sat. Fat:** 6g   **Salt:** 2.8g   **Carb.:** 17g
Cook: No cooking   **Prep:** 10 min.

Serves 1

Dressing

1 tablespoon red wine vinegar

1 tablespoon water

½ teaspoon Dijon mustard

⅛ teaspoon salt

⅛ teaspoon pepper

2 teaspoons olive oil

Salad

2 tablespoons chickpeas

4 pitted Kalamata olives, diced

¼ cucumber, peeled, seeded, and diced

5 small cherry tomatoes, halved

2 cups chopped romaine lettuce

¼ cup crumbled vegetarian feta cheese

1 To make the dressing, combine the ingredients in a small bowl or jar with a lid and whisk or shake until emulsified.

2 In a portable container with a lid, layer the salad ingredients, beginning with the dressing. Next add the chickpeas, then the olives, cucumber, tomatoes, lettuce, and cheese. Chill upright until ready to serve.

3 To serve, shake the container vigorously to toss the salad. Transfer to a serving plate and serve immediately.

squash & couscous salad

Stay Fuller For Longer

Vegan

Calories: 200 **Fat:** 8.5g **Sat. Fat:** 1.1g **Salt:** 0.14g **Carb.:** 28g
Cook: 25 min. **Prep:** 25 min.

Serves 4

1 butternut squash, seeded, peeled, and cut into small chunks

1 onion, coarsely chopped

1 garlic clove, crushed (optional)

2 tablespoons olive oil

⅔ cup couscous

4 sun-dried tomatoes in oil, drained and chopped

1 cup boiling water

3 tablespoons chopped fresh parsley

1 tablespoon lemon juice

salt and pepper

1 Preheat the oven to 400°F. Place the squash, onion, garlic (if using), and oil in a roasting pan. Toss together. Cover the pan tightly with aluminum foil and bake in the preheated oven for 20–25 minutes, or until the vegetables are just tender. Let stand for 5 minutes before removing the foil.

2 While the vegetables are cooking, place the couscous and sun-dried tomatoes in a heatproof bowl. Pour the boiling water over the couscous, then cover the bowl and let stand for about 10 minutes, or until all the liquid is absorbed.

3 Fluff up the couscous with a fork. Add the couscous mixture to the vegetables and their juices in the roasting pan with the parsley and lemon juice. Season with salt and pepper, then gently toss together. Serve warm or cold.

shrimp taco salad

Quick & Easy

Calories: 286   **Fat:** 8g   **Sat. Fat:** 1g   **Salt:** 3.2g   **Carb.:** 4g
Cook: 10 min.   **Prep:** 15 min.

Serves 4

Salad

2 corn tortillas

1 spray of vegetable oil spray

2 teaspoons salt

1 pound shrimp, peeled and deveined, thawed if frozen

6 cups chopped romaine lettuce

1 cucumber, sliced

1 cup corn kernels, thawed if frozen

2 tomatoes, cut into wedges

Dressing

2 tablespoons olive oil

2 tablespoons lime juice

1 garlic clove, finely chopped

½ teaspoon ground cumin

½ teaspoon salt

1 tablespoon diced red onion

1 tablespoon finely chopped cilantro

1 Preheat the oven to 400°F. Line a large baking sheet with aluminum foil.

2 Spray the tortillas on both sides with vegetable oil. Cut them in half, then cut the halves into ¼-inch wide strips. Put the strips in a single layer on the prepared baking sheet and bake for about 10 minutes, or until crisp and lightly browned. Remove from the oven and let cool on the baking sheet.

3 While the tortilla strips bake, put 4 cups of water and the salt in a large saucepan and bring it to a boil over high heat. Add the shrimp, reduce the heat to medium, and simmer for about 4 minutes, or until the shrimp are cooked through. Drain the shrimp, put them in a bowl, and refrigerate until ready to use.

4 To make the dressing, whisk together the olive oil, lime juice, garlic, cumin, and salt until emulsified. Stir in the onion and cilantro and mix well.

5 In a large bowl, combine the lettuce, cucumber, corn, and tomatoes and toss well. Add several spoonfuls of the dressing and toss to coat. Divide the salad evenly among four serving plates. Top each with the cooked shrimp, and drizzle with some of the dressing. Garnish with the tortilla strips and serve immediately.

chicken & spicy peanut salad

Calories: 296   **Fat:** 12g   **Sat. Fat:** 2.5g   **Salt:** 0.9g   **Carb.:** 16g

Cook: No cooking   **Prep:** 10 min.

Serves 4

⅓ cup reduced-fat chunky peanut butter

2 tablespoons lemon juice

1 garlic clove, finely chopped

1 tablespoon finely chopped fresh ginger

2 teaspoons sesame oil

1 tablespoon brown sugar

1 tablespoon gluten-free tamari (soy sauce)

1 tablespoon water

¼–½ teaspoon cayenne pepper

2 tablespoons finely chopped cilantro, plus extra to garnish

2 scallions, thinly sliced

4 cups chopped romaine lettuce

1 cucumber, sliced

1 small red, yellow, or orange bell pepper, seeded and diced

2½ cups diced cooked skinless, boneless chicken breast

1 In a small bowl, combine the peanut butter, lemon juice, garlic, ginger, sesame oil, brown sugar, tamari, water, and cayenne. Stir well. Stir in the cilantro and scallions.

2 In a large serving bowl, toss the lettuce, cucumber, and bell pepper. Add a few spoonfuls of the peanut dressing and toss to coat. Divide the salad among four serving plates or bowls. Top with the chicken, then drizzle with more of the dressing. Garnish with finely chopped cilantro and serve immediately.

sweet potato soup

Calories: 182 **Fat:** 8.5g **Sat. Fat:** 6.5g **Salt:** 1g **Carb.:** 25g
Cook: 30 min. **Prep:** 5 min.

Serves 6

2 teaspoons vegetable oil

1 onion, diced

1 tablespoon finely chopped fresh ginger

1 tablespoon vegan gluten-free
Thai red curry paste

1 teaspoon salt

4 orange-fleshed sweet potatoes
(about 1½ pounds), peeled and diced

1 (14-ounce) can light coconut milk

4 cups gluten-free vegetable stock

juice of 1 lime

½ cup finely chopped fresh cilantro,
to garnish

1 In a large, heavy saucepan, heat the oil over medium–high heat. Add the onion and ginger and cook, stirring, for about 5 minutes, or until soft. Add the curry paste and salt and cook, stirring, for another minute or so. Add the sweet potatoes, coconut milk, and vegetable stock and bring to a boil. Reduce the heat to medium and simmer, uncovered, for about 20 minutes, or until the sweet potatoes are soft.

2 Puree the soup, either in batches in a blender or food processor or using a handheld immersion blender. Return the soup to the heat and bring back up to a simmer. Just before serving, stir in the lime juice. Serve hot, garnished with cilantro.

roasted tomato soup

Vegetarian

Calories: 263   **Fat:** 15g   **Sat. Fat:** 3.5g   **Salt:** 2g   **Carb.:** 26g
Cook: 1¼ hr.   **Prep:** 25 min.

Serves 4

3 pounds Roma tomatoes, halved, stem ends removed

1 red onion, coarsely chopped

6 garlic cloves, peeled

2 tablespoons olive oil

¾ teaspoon salt

1 teaspoon pepper

6 sprigs fresh thyme

4 cups vegetable stock

2 tablespoons lemon juice

Parmesan croutons

2 cups cubed whole-wheat sourdough bread

2 tablespoons olive oil

½ teaspoon salt

½ teaspoon pepper

2 tablespoons vegetarian Parmesan-style cheese

1 Preheat the oven to 450°F. On a large baking sheet, toss the tomatoes, onion, and garlic with the olive oil, salt, pepper, and thyme. Spread the vegetables out into a single layer, arranging the tomatoes cut side up, and roast in the preheated oven for about 45 minutes, or until the vegetables are soft.

2 To make the croutons, reduce the oven heat to 300°F. Toss the cubed bread with the olive oil and sprinkle with the salt and pepper. Spread the bread cubes in an even layer on a baking sheet and bake in the preheated oven for about 25 minutes. Sprinkle with the cheese, return to the oven, and bake for another 5 minutes, or until cheese is melted and beginning to brown.

3 Finish the soup while the croutons are baking. In several batches in a blender or food processor, or using a handheld immersion blender, puree the vegetables along with the stock.

4 Bring the puree to a boil in a large saucepan over high heat. Reduce the heat to medium and simmer, stirring occasionally, for about 15 minutes. Just before serving, stir in the lemon juice. Serve hot, garnished with croutons.

chicken noodle soup

Stay Fuller For Longer

Calories: 292   **Fat:** 3.5g   **Sat. Fat:** 0.5g   **Salt:** 1.6g   **Carb.:** 31.5g
Cook: 25–30 min.   **Prep:** 15 min.

Serves 6

1 tablespoon olive oil

1 onion, diced

4 garlic cloves, finely chopped

2 carrots, diced

2 celery stalks, diced

6 cups chicken stock

4 sprigs fresh thyme

1 bay leaf

1 teaspoon salt

½ teaspoon pepper, plus extra to garnish

1 pound skinless, boneless chicken breasts

8 ounces dried pasta

grated zest and juice of 1 lemon

1 In a large, heavy saucepan, heat the olive oil over medium–high heat. Add the onion and garlic and sauté, stirring frequently, for about 5 minutes, or until soft. Add the carrots and celery and cook for another 1–2 minutes. Add the stock, thyme, bay leaf, salt, and pepper and bring to a boil.

2 Reduce heat to medium–low and add the chicken breasts. Simmer for about 20 minutes, or until the chicken is cooked through without any signs of pink when the thickest part of the meat is cut through with a sharp knife. Remove the chicken from the pan and set aside. When cool enough to handle, cut the chicken into bite-size pieces.

3 Remove the thyme sprigs and bay leaf from the soup and discard them. Return the soup to a simmer over medium heat.

4 Cook the pasta according to the package directions and drain. Add the cooked pasta and cooked chicken to the soup and simmer for about 5 minutes, or until heated through. Just before serving, stir in the lemon zest and juice.

5 Serve immediately, garnished with freshly ground pepper.

chicken tacos

Calories: 300 **Fat:** 2g **Sat. Fat:** 0.5g **Salt:** 1.6g **Carb.:** 43.5g
Cook: 15 min. **Prep:** 20 min.

Serves 4

Salsa

½ red onion, diced

2 jalapeno peppers, seeded and diced

4 tomatoes, diced

¼ cup chopped cilantro

3 tablespoons lime juice

½ teaspoon salt

Chicken filling

2 teaspoons packed brown sugar

2 teaspoons ground cumin

1 teaspoon chili powder

½ teaspoon salt

½ teaspoon pepper

14 ounces skinless, boneless chicken breasts

8 small corn tortillas (1 ounce each), to serve

2 cups shredded lettuce, to serve

1 Make the salsa by putting the onion, jalapeno peppers, and tomatoes into a medium bowl and stirring well. Add the cilantro, lime juice, and salt and stir to combine.

2 To make the chicken filling, preheat the broiler to high or put a griddle pan over high heat. In a small bowl, combine the brown sugar, cumin, chili powder, salt, and pepper. Rub the spice mixture all over the chicken breasts. Broil the chicken breasts over high heat for about 4 minutes per side, or until lightly browned on the outside and cooked through with no signs of pink when cut through with a sharp knife. Remove from heat and let stand about 5 minutes, then slice into ¼-inch thick slices.

3 To serve, heat the tortillas briefly on the broiler, then top with the chicken, salsa, and lettuce. Serve immediately.

stuffed eggplant

Vegetarian

Calories: 287   **Fat:** 14g   **Sat. Fat:** 4.2g   **Salt:** 2.1g   **Carb.:** 29g
Cook: 45 min.   **Prep:** 15 min.

Serves 4

2 small–medium eggplants

1 tablespoon olive oil

1 small onion, diced

2 garlic cloves, finely chopped

⅔ cup quinoa

1½ cups vegetable stock

1 teaspoon salt

pinch of pepper

2 tablespoons slivered almonds, toasted

3 tablespoons finely chopped fresh mint

½ cup crumbled vegetarian feta cheese

1 Preheat the oven to 450°F. Place the eggplants on a baking sheet and bake in the oven for 15 minutes, or until soft.

2 Meanwhile, heat the olive oil in a large, heavy skillet over medium–high heat. Add the onion and garlic and cook, stirring occasionally, for about 5 minutes, or until soft. Add the quinoa, stock, salt, and pepper.

3 When the eggplants are soft, remove from the oven and let cool slightly. Cut each in half lengthwise and scoop out the flesh, leaving a ¼-inch thick border inside the skin so they hold their shape. Chop the flesh and stir it into the quinoa mixture in the skillet. Reduce the heat to medium–low, cover, and cook for about 15 minutes, or until the quinoa is cooked through. Remove from the heat and stir in the almonds, 2 tablespoons of the mint, and half the cheese.

4 Stuff the quinoa mixture equally among the eggplant skins and top with the remaining cheese. Bake in the oven for about 10–15 minutes, or until the cheese is bubbling and beginning to brown. Garnish with the remaining mint and serve.

falafel pita pockets

Calories: 221 **Fat:** 5g **Sat. Fat:** 1g **Salt:** 2g **Carb.:** 35g

Cook: 10 min. **Prep:** 15 min.

Serves 4

2 garlic cloves

2 tablespoons each of chopped flat-leaf parsley and cilantro

1 teaspoon ground cumin

½ teaspoon salt

2 cups canned chickpeas, drained and rinsed

2 scallions, sliced

2 tablespoons all-purpose flour

1 teaspoon baking powder

1 tablespoon vegetable oil

Tzatziki sauce

1 small cucumber, peeled, seeded, and grated

½ teaspoon salt

½ cup plain, nonfat yogurt

2 tablespoons lemon juice

2 tablespoons chopped fresh mint leaves

To serve

2 whole-wheat pitas, halved and warmed

2 tomatoes, diced

2 cups shredded lettuce

1 To make the falafel patties, chop the garlic in a food processor. Add the parsley, cilantro, cumin, and salt and process until the herbs are finely chopped. Add the chickpeas, scallions, flour, and baking powder and process until the texture resembles coarse bread crumbs. Form the falafel mixture into eight patties, about ¼-inch thick.

2 To make the sauce, put the grated cucumber on a double layer of paper towels and sprinkle with half the salt. Set aside. In a medium bowl, combine the yogurt, the remaining salt, lemon juice, and mint and stir to combine. Bundle the cucumber up in the paper towels and, holding over the sink, squeeze out the excess juice. Mix the cucumber into the yogurt mixture. Chill until ready to serve.

3 In a heavy skillet, heat the oil over medium–high heat. When the oil is hot, add the patties and cook about 3 minutes, or until browned on the bottom. Turn over and cook until browned on the other side. Drain on paper towels.

4 To serve, stuff two falafel patties into each pita half, drizzle with some of the sauce, then add diced tomato and shredded lettuce. Serve immediately.

roasted vegetable melts

Vegetarian

Quick & Easy

Calories: 225　**Fat:** 10.5g　**Sat. Fat:** 5.5g　**Salt:** 1.4g　**Carb.:** 24g
Cook: 20 min.　**Prep:** 10 min.

Serves 4

2 sprays of olive oil spray

1 red bell pepper, seeded and cut into strips

1 small eggplant, sliced into ½-inch circles

2 small zucchini, sliced lengthwise into ½-inch thick strips

4 garlic cloves, peeled but left whole

½ teaspoon pepper

½ teaspoon salt

4 slices sourdough bread, toasted

4 ounces vegetarian fontina or Swiss cheese, thinly sliced

1 Preheat the oven to 450°F. Spray a large baking sheet with olive oil.

2 Arrange the bell pepper, eggplant, zucchini, and whole garlic cloves in a single layer on the prepared baking sheet. Spray with more of the olive oil to coat evenly and sprinkle with the pepper. Roast in preheated oven for about 20 minutes, until the vegetables soften and begin to brown. Remove the vegetables from the oven, but leave the oven on.

3 In a small bowl, mash together the roasted garlic and salt into a paste. Spread the paste on the toast slices. Top each slice with one-quarter of the roasted vegetables. Finally, top each with a layer of cheese.

4 Put the vegetable-topped toasts on the baking sheet and return to the preheated oven. Cook for about 4 minutes, or until the cheese melts. Serve immediately.

turkey-avocado & blt wrap

Quick & Easy

Calories: 247   **Fat:** 14g   **Sat. Fat:** 3g   **Salt:** 2.4g   **Carb.:** 4g
Cook: 5–7 min.   **Prep:** 5 min.

Serves 2

1 spray of vegetable oil spray

4 slices turkey bacon

2 tablespoons reduced-fat mayonnaise

4 large romaine lettuce leaves

4 ounces deli-sliced turkey breast

½ tomato, cut into wedges

½ small avocado, sliced

1 Spray a nonstick skillet with the vegetable oil spray and heat it over medium–high heat. Add the turkey bacon and cook, turning once, for about 2–3 minutes per side, or until lightly browned and crisp.

2 Spread the mayonnaise down the center of each lettuce leaf. Lay the turkey breast slices into the lettuce leaves, then the bacon, tomato, and avocado, dividing all ingredients equally. Wrap up and serve immediately.

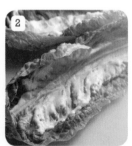

crab salad sandwiches

Quick & Easy

Calories: 300   **Fat:** 10g   **Sat. Fat:** 1g   **Salt:** 2.3g   **Carb.:** 30.5g

Cook: 2–4 min.   **Prep:** 10 min.

Serves 4

1 small fennel bulb with leaves

14 ounces crabmeat, picked over

2 tablespoons low-fat mayonnaise

2 celery stalks, finely chopped

2 scallions, thinly sliced

1 tablespoon lemon juice

½ teaspoon salt

8 slices whole-wheat bread

1 Remove the leaves from the fennel bulb, then chop and reserve 1 teaspoon of the leaves. Slice the bulb in half lengthwise, the carefully cut each half into paper-thin slices and set aside.

2 In a small bowl, combine the crabmeat, mayonnaise, celery, scallions, fennel leaves, lemon juice, and salt. Stir to mix well.

3 Toast the bread. Divide the crab mixture evenly among four slices of the toasted bread. Top with the paper-thin fennel slices and the remaining four slices of bread. Cut each sandwich in half diagonally and serve immediately.

green salad with yogurt dressing

Vegetarian
Quick & Easy

Calories: 109   **Fat:** 7g   **Sat. Fat:** 1.5g   **Salt:** 0.2g   **Carb.:** 19g
Cook: No cooking   **Prep:** 15 min.

Serves 4

½ cucumber, sliced

6 scallions, chopped

2 tomatoes, sliced

1 yellow bell pepper, seeded and cut into strips

2 celery stalks, cut into strips

4 radishes, sliced

3 cups arugula

1 tablespoon chopped fresh mint, to garnish (optional)

Dressing

2 tablespoons lemon juice

1 garlic clove, crushed

⅓ cup low-fat natural yogurt

2 tablespoons olive oil

salt and pepper

1 To make the salad, gently mix the cucumber, scallions, tomatoes, yellow bell pepper strips, celery, radishes, and arugula in a large serving bowl.

2 To make the dressing, stir the lemon juice, garlic, natural yogurt, and olive oil together in a small bowl until thoroughly combined. Season with salt and pepper to taste.

3 Spoon the dressing over the salad and toss to mix. Garnish the salad with chopped mint (if using) and serve immediately.

Chapter 3
Dinner

fish tacos with avocado salsa

Quick & Easy

Calories: 300 **Fat:** 14g **Sat. Fat:** 1g **Salt:** 1.3g **Carb.:** 22g
Cook: 5–10 min. **Prep:** 15 min.

Serves 4

Salsa

½ red onion, diced

2 jalapeno peppers, seeded and diced

2 tomatoes, diced

½ avocado, diced

2 tablespoons chopped cilantro

3 tablespoons lime juice

½ teaspoon salt

Fish

2 tablespoons lime juice

1 tablespoon olive oil

1 teaspoon ground cumin

1 teaspoon chili powder

½ teaspoon salt

14 ounces sole fillet

To serve

8 small corn tortillas (1 ounce each)

2 cups shredded red cabbage

1 Put all the salsa ingredients in a medium bowl and stir to mix well.

2 Heat a broiler to medium–high or put a griddle pan over medium–high heat. In a small bowl, combine the lime juice, olive oil, cumin, chili powder, and salt. Brush the mixture on both sides of the fish fillets. Broil the fish over medium–high heat for about 2–4 minutes per side, or until broiler marks start to appear and the fish is opaque and cooked through.

3 To serve, warm the tortillas under the broiler, then top them with the fish, salsa, and shredded cabbage. Serve immediately.

butternut squash & lentil stew

Wheat, Gluten & Dairy Free

Vegan

Calories: 234 **Fat:** 8g **Sat. Fat:** 0.8g **Salt:** 1.6g **Carb.:** 26.5g
Cook: 30 min. **Prep:** 10 min.

Serves 4

1 tablespoon olive oil

1 onion, diced

3 garlic cloves, finely chopped

2 tablespoons tomato paste

2 teaspoons ground cumin

1 teaspoon ground cinnamon

1 teaspoon salt

¼ teaspoon cayenne pepper

1 pound butternut squash, diced

½ cup brown lentils

2 cups gluten-free vegetable stock

1 tablespoon lemon juice

¼ cup nonfat plain soya yogurt, to garnish

2 tablespoons finely chopped cilantro, to garnish

2 tablespoons slivered almonds, to garnish

1 Heat the oil in a large saucepan or small stockpot over medium–high heat. Add the onion and garlic and cook, stirring occasionally, for about 5 minutes, or until soft.

2 Add the tomato paste, cumin, cinnamon, salt, and cayenne and give it a quick stir. Add the squash, lentils, and stock and bring to a boil. Reduce the heat to low and simmer, uncovered, stirring occasionally, for about 25 minutes, until the squash and lentils are tender.

3 Just before serving, stir in the lemon juice. Serve hot, garnished with a dollop of the yogurt and a sprinkling of the cilantro and almonds.

sweet & sour noodles

Vegetarian

Quick & Easy

Calories: 254 Fat: 6g Sat. Fat: 1.5g Salt: 2.3g Carb.: 40g
Cook: 12–15 min. Prep: 10 min.

Serves 4

5 ounces dried medium egg noodles

2 teaspoons sunflower oil

1 large red bell pepper, seeded and thinly sliced

1½ cups bean sprouts

5 scallions, thinly sliced

3 tablespoons Chinese rice wine or dry sherry

salt

Sauce

3 tablespoons light soy sauce

2 tablespoons honey

2 tablespoons tomato paste

2 teaspoons cornstarch

2 teaspoons sesame oil

½ cup vegetable stock

1 Bring a large saucepan of lightly salted water to a boil. Add the noodles, bring back to a boil, and cook according to the package directions, until tender but still firm to the bite. Drain.

2 To make the sauce, put the soy sauce, honey, tomato paste, cornstarch, and sesame oil into a small bowl and mix together until smooth, then stir in the stock.

3 Heat the sunflower oil in a large wok or heavy skillet. Add the red bell pepper and stir-fry for 4 minutes, until soft. Add the bean sprouts and stir-fry for 1 minute. Add the noodles and scallions, then pour the wine and sauce over the the vegetables and noodles. Toss together over the heat for 1–2 minutes, until the sauce is bubbling and thickened and the noodles are heated all the way through. Serve immediately.

white chicken chili

Calories: 219   Fat: 5.5g   Sat. Fat: 1g   Salt: 1.1g   Carb.: 10g
Cook: 35–40 min.   Prep: 10 min.

Serves 6

1 tablespoon vegetable oil

1 onion, diced

2 garlic cloves, finely chopped

1 green bell pepper, seeded and diced

1 small jalapeno pepper, seeded and diced

2 teaspoons chili powder

2 teaspoons dried oregano

1 teaspoon ground cumin

1 teaspoon salt

1 (15-ounce) can white beans, such as
cannellini, rinsed and drained

3 cups gluten-free chicken stock

1 pound cooked chicken breasts, shredded

juice of 1 lime

⅓ cup chopped cilantro

1 Heat the oil in a large, heavy saucepan over medium–high heat. Add the onion, garlic, bell pepper, and jalapeno and cook, stirring occasionally, for about 5 minutes, or until soft. Add the chili powder, oregano, cumin, and salt and cook, stirring, for about another 30 seconds. Add the beans and stock and bring to a boil. Reduce the heat to medium–low and simmer gently, uncovered, for about 20 minutes.

2 Ladle about half of the bean mixture into a blender or food processor and puree. Return the puree to the pan along with the shredded chicken. Simmer for about 10 minutes, or until heated through. Just before serving, stir in the lime juice and cilantro. Serve immediately.

spaghetti with bacon-tomato sauce

Stay Fuller For Longer

Calories: 300   **Fat:** 6g   **Sat. Fat:** 2g   **Salt:** 1g   **Carb.:** 52g
Cook: 25 min.   **Prep:** 10 min.

Serves 6

2 bacon strips (2 ounces total)

1 shallot, diced

2 garlic cloves, finely chopped

¼ cup red wine

½ teaspoon salt

½ teaspoon pepper

1 (28-ounce) can diced tomatoes, with juice

15 ounces whole-wheat spaghetti

2 tablespoons grated Parmesan cheese

1 Heat a large skillet over medium–high heat. Add the bacon and cook for about 3 minutes on each side, or until crisp. Drain the strips on a paper towel, then crumble and set aside.

2 Remove the excess bacon grease from the skillet, leaving about 2 teaspoons. Add the shallot and garlic and cook, stirring occasionally, over medium–high heat for about 5 minutes, or until soft. Add the wine, salt, and pepper and bring to a boil. Add the cooked bacon along with the tomatoes and their juice and bring to a boil. Reduce the heat to medium and simmer, uncovered, for about 20 minutes.

3 While the sauce simmers, cook the spaghetti in a large saucepan of boiling water according to the package directions, until tender to the bite. Drain.

4 Divide the pasta among six wide pasta bowls, top with the tomato sauce, garnish with the cheese, and serve immediately.

roasted pork with gingered apples

Wheat, Gluten & Dairy Free

Calories: 220   **Fat:** 4.5g   **Sat. Fat:** 1.5g   **Salt:** 0.8g   **Carb.:** 25g

Cook: 45 min.   **Prep:** 15 min. plus marinating

Serves 4

2 garlic cloves

½ cup red wine

2 tablespoons packed brown sugar

1 tablespoon gluten-free tamari (soy sauce)

1 teaspoon sesame oil

½ teaspoon ground cinnamon

¼ teaspoon ground cloves

1 star anise pod, broken into pieces

½ teaspoon pepper

12 ounces pork tenderloin

steamed green beans, to serve

Gingered apples

4 Granny Smith apples, diced

1 tablespoon rice vinegar

1 tablespoon brown sugar

¼ cup apple juice

1 tablespoon fresh ginger, finely chopped

1 In a bowl large enough to hold the pork, combine the garlic, wine, brown sugar, tamari, sesame oil, cinnamon, cloves, star anise, and pepper. Add the pork and toss to coat. Cover and refrigerate for at least 2 hours or overnight.

2 Preheat the oven to 375°F. Heat a nonstick skillet over high heat. Remove the pork from the marinade, letting any excess run off into the bowl. Sear the pork, turning occasionally, in the hot skillet for about 8 minutes, or until browned on all sides.

3 Place the meat in an ovenproof dish and drizzle with a few spoonfuls of the marinade. Roast in the preheated oven for 15 minutes. Turn the meat over, drizzle with more of the marinade, and continue to roast for about another 30 minutes, or until cooked through. A meat thermometer should have a reading of 160°F. Or insert the tip of a sharp knife into the center of the meat and check that there is no pink meat.

4 While the meat is roasting, make the gingered apples. In a saucepan, combine the apples, vinegar, sugar, apple juice, and ginger. Cook over medium–high heat, stirring occasionally, until the liquid begins to boil. Reduce the heat to medium–low and simmer, stirring occasionally, for about 20 minutes, or until the apples are soft and the liquid is mostly evaporated.

5 Once the pork has cooked, remove it from the oven and cover the baking dish in a "tent" of aluminum foil. Let the meat rest for about 5 minutes. Slice the meat into ¼-inch thick slices and serve with a spoonful of the gingered apples alongside and the green beans.

chipotle-lime shrimp burgers

Quick & Easy

Calories: 300   **Fat:** 7.5g   **Sat. Fat:** 1.1g   **Salt:** 3.3g   **Carb.:** 31g
Cook: 6–8 min.   **Prep:** 10–15 min.

Serves 4

1¼ pounds shrimp, peeled and deveined

1 celery stalk, finely diced

2 scallions, finely chopped

2 tablespoons finely chopped cilantro

1 garlic clove, finely chopped

½ teaspoon salt

½ teaspoon ground chipotle

zest and juice of 1 lime

2 teaspoons olive oil

2 tablespoons reduced-fat mayonnaise

4 small whole-wheat burger buns, toasted

4 lettuce leaves

1 Process 1 pound of the shrimp in a food processor. Dice the remaining ¼ pound of shrimp. In a medium bowl, combine the pureed and diced shrimp. Add the celery, scallions, cilantro, garlic, salt, ground chipotle, and lime zest and juice and mix well. Form the mixture into four patties.

2 Heat the oil in a large, nonstick skillet over medium–high heat. Add the shrimp patties and cook for about 3–4 minutes, or until browned on the bottom. Flip the patties over and cook for another 3–4 minutes, or until browned and cooked through.

3 Spread the mayonnaise onto the bottom halves of the buns, dividing evenly. Place one shrimp burger on the bottom half of each bun, then top with a lettuce leaf and the top half of the bun. Serve immediately.

crab cakes

Calories: 225   **Fat:** 14g   **Sat. Fat:** 2g   **Salt:** 2.4g   **Carb.:** 9g
Cook: 30 min.   **Prep:** 10 min.

Serves 4

Crab cakes

2 sprays of vegetable oil spray

1 pound crabmeat

1 egg, lightly beaten

1 tablespoon reduced-fat mayonnaise

1 teaspoon Dijon mustard

1 teaspoon Worcestershire sauce

1 tablespoon lemon juice

2 tablespoons chopped chives

1/4 teaspoon salt

3/4 cup bread crumbs

Caper mayonnaise

1/4 cup reduced-fat mayonnaise

2 teaspoons capers, finely chopped

zest of 1 lemon

1 Preheat the oven to 400°F. Spray a large baking sheet with the vegetable oil spray.

2 In a medium bowl, combine the crabmeat, egg, mayonnaise, mustard, Worcestershire sauce, lemon juice, chives, salt, and 1/4 cup of the bread crumbs. Stir to mix well.

3 Put the remaining bread crumbs on a plate or in a shallow bowl. Form the crab mixture into eight patties about 2½ inches in diameter and coat them on all sides with bread crumbs. Put the patties on the prepared baking sheet and spray the tops with vegetable oil spray. Bake in the preheated oven for about 30 minutes, or until browned and crisp.

4 Meanwhile, make the mayonnaise. Put all the ingredients into a small bowl and stir to mix well. Serve the crab cakes hot, with a spoonful of caper mayonnaise.

3

3

4

broccoli pizza

Vegetarian

Calories: 274   Fat: 9g   Sat. Fat: 4g   Salt: 1.3g   Carb.: 40.5g
Cook: 18 min.   Prep: 20 min. plus rising

Serves 8

Dough

1 cup warm (105–110°F) water

1½ teaspoons active dry yeast

2 teaspoons salt

1 teaspoon sugar

1 tablespoon olive oil

3 cups bread flour, plus extra for dusting

2 sprays of olive oil spray

Topping

2 cups small broccoli florets

2 teaspoons olive oil

1 red onion, thinly sliced

1 garlic clove, finely chopped

1 tablespoon chopped fresh oregano

1¼ cups shredded vegetarian Swiss cheese

¼–½ teaspoon crushed red pepper flakes

1 To make the pizza dough, combine the warm water, yeast, salt, and sugar in a large mixing bowl and stir well. Let stand for about 10 minutes, or until bubbly. Stir in the olive oil, then gradually mix in the flour with an electric mixer or food processor until the dough comes together in a ball. Invert the dough onto a lightly floured surface and knead, adding a little more flour if needed, for a minute or two, or until firm. Wash and dry the mixing bowl, then spray with olive oil. Put the dough in the bowl, cover with plastic wrap, and let rise in a warm place for about an hour, until doubled in size.

2 Preheat the oven to 450°F. Spray a large baking sheet with olive oil. Roll out the pizza dough into a large rectangle and place it on the prepared baking sheet. Bake in the preheated oven for about 8 minutes, or until just beginning to brown.

3 Meanwhile, put the broccoli in a microwave-safe bowl along with ¼ cup of water and cover tightly with plastic wrap. Microwave on high for about 3 minutes, or until the broccoli is just tender. Drain and chop the broccoli into small pieces.

4 Heat the olive oil in a skillet over medium heat. Add the onion and garlic. Cook, stirring occasionally, for about 5 minutes, or until soft. Remove from the heat and stir in the oregano. Spread the onion mixture evenly onto the part-baked pizza crust and top it with the broccoli, then sprinkle with the cheese and red pepper flakes. Bake for about 10 minutes, or until the cheese is melted, bubbling, and golden brown. Slice and serve immediately.

chicken & vegetable enchiladas

Calories: 296 **Fat:** 7.5g **Sat. Fat:** 3g **Salt:** 2g **Carb.:** 35g
Cook: 50 min. **Prep:** 15 min.

Serves 4

2 sprays of olive oil spray

2 zucchini, diced (about 3 cups)

1 red bell pepper, seeded and diced

1 teaspoon salt

1 onion, diced

2 garlic cloves, finely chopped

1 tablespoon chili powder

1 tablespoon dried oregano

¾ cup tomato sauce

1 cup vegetable stock

6 ounces cooked chicken breast, shredded

8 small corn tortillas (1 ounce each)

⅔ cup shredded 50% reduced-fat cheddar cheese

1 Preheat the oven to 450°F. Spray a large, rimmed baking sheet with half a spray of olive oil spray.

2 Spread the zucchini and bell pepper on the prepared baking sheet and spray with half a spray of olive oil spray. Sprinkle with half of the salt. Bake in the preheated oven for about 20 minutes, or until soft and beginning to brown.

3 Meanwhile, spray a large skillet with 1 spray of olive oil and place over medium–high heat. Add the onion and garlic and cook, stirring, for about 5 minutes, or until soft. Add the chili powder and oregano and cook for another minute. Add the tomato sauce and stock and bring to a boil. Reduce the heat to medium and simmer, stirring occasionally, for 5 minutes. Stir in the remaining salt. Puree the sauce, in batches, in a blender or food processor, or use an immersion blender.

4 When the vegetables are done, remove them from the oven and reduce the heat to 350°F. In a large bowl, combine the vegetables, shredded chicken, and several spoonfuls of the sauce. Stir well.

5 Coat the bottom of a 9 x 13-inch baking dish with a thin layer of the sauce. Place four of the tortillas on the bottom of the dish, overlapping as little as possible. Top the tortillas with the chicken-vegetable mixture and then a second layer of four tortillas. Top the stacks with the remaining sauce, then sprinkle the cheese over the top.

6 Bake in the preheated oven for about 30 minutes, until the enchiladas are heated through and the cheese is bubbling and beginning to brown. Serve immediately.

chicken & sun-dried tomato pasta

Stay Fuller For Longer

Calories: 297 **Fat:** 4g **Sat. Fat:** 0.6g **Salt:** 1.7g **Carb.:** 48.2g
Cook: 15–20 min. **Prep:** 25 min.

Serves 6

3¾ ounces of sun-dried tomatoes (not packed in oil)

12 ounces boneless, skinless chicken breasts, diced

1 teaspoon salt

½ teaspoon pepper

1 spray of vegetable oil spray

2 garlic cloves

½ cup fresh basil

1 tablespoon olive oil

10½ ounces dried pasta

1 Put the tomatoes in a small bowl and cover with boiling water. Set aside to soak for about 20 minutes, until soft, then drain, discarding the soaking liquid.

2 Season the chicken with ½ teaspoon of the salt and the pepper. Coat a large, nonstick skillet with the vegetable oil spray and heat over medium–high heat. Add the chicken and cook, stirring occasionally, for about 5 minutes, or until it is cooked through and just beginning to brown. Set aside.

3 Place the rehydrated tomatoes in a food processor along with the garlic and basil and process to a paste. Add the oil and the remaining salt and continue to process until smooth.

4 Cook the pasta according to the package directions. Just before draining, scoop out and reserve about ½ cup of the cooking water. Drain the pasta.

5 Toss the hot pasta with the sun-dried tomato pesto, chicken, and as much of the pasta cooking water as needed to make a sauce to coat the pasta. Serve immediately.

halibut with romesco sauce

Quick & Easy

Calories: 261   **Fat:** 7g   **Sat. Fat:** 1g   **Salt:** 1.4g   **Carb.:** 10g
Cook: 15 min.   **Prep:** 10 min.

Serves 4

1½ pounds halibut fillets

¾ teaspoon salt

½ teaspoon pepper

Sauce

1 large red bell pepper

3 garlic cloves, peeled

½ cup slivered, toasted almonds

1 thick slice of bread, torn into a few pieces

1 teaspoon salt

1 teaspoon paprika

1 cup drained canned diced tomatoes

2 tablespoons red wine vinegar

1 To make the sauce, preheat the broiler. Quarter the bell pepper and place it, cut side down, on a baking sheet along with the garlic cloves. Broil, turning the garlic once, until the garlic is browned and soft and the skin of the bell pepper blackens and blisters. Remove from the broiler and set aside to cool slightly.

2 When cool enough to handle, peel the blackened skin from the pepper and remove the core and seeds, discarding both. Put the bell pepper and garlic in a food processor along with the almonds, bread, salt, and paprika. Process to a paste. Add the tomatoes and vinegar and process until the tomatoes are smooth and fully incorporated.

3 To cook the fish, preheat a broiler to high or heat a ridged grill pan over high heat. Season the fish with the salt and pepper and broil for about 4 minutes. Turn and broil on the second side for about another 4 minutes, or until the fish is opaque and cooked through. Serve the fish immediately, with the sauce drizzled over it and green vegetables, if desired.

shrimp & sausage jambalaya

Calories: 270 **Fat:** 6g **Sat. Fat:** 2g **Salt:** 1.8g **Carb.:** 27g
Cook: 40–45 min. **Prep:** 10 min.

Serves 6

1 tablespoon olive oil

1 onion, diced

2 garlic cloves, finely chopped

1 green bell pepper, seeded and diced

2 celery stalks, diced

3/4 cup long-grain white rice

1 tablespoon paprika

2 teaspoons dried oregano

2 teaspoons dried thyme

1 teaspoon salt

1/2 teaspoon cayenne pepper, or to taste

1/2 teaspoon pepper

1 (14-ounce) can diced tomatoes, drained

3 cups chicken stock

1 bay leaf

1 pound shrimp, peeled, deveined, and chopped, thawed if frozen

4 ounces Andouille sausage or spicy Italian-style sausage, diced

1 Heat the oil in a large, heavy saucepan over medium–high heat. Add the onion, garlic, bell pepper, and celery and cook, stirring occasionally, for about 5 minutes, or until soft.

2 Add the rice, paprika, oregano, thyme, salt, cayenne, and pepper and cook for about another 30 seconds. Add the tomatoes, stock, and bay leaf. Reduce the heat to medium, cover, and cook, stirring occasionally, for about 25–30 minutes, or until the rice is tender.

3 Stir in the shrimp and sausage and cook, uncovered, for about 6–8 minutes, or until the shrimp are cooked through. Remove and discard the bay leaf. Serve immediately.

spicy corn chowder

Calories: 156   **Fat:** 8g   **Sat. Fat:** 1g   **Salt:** 0.7g   **Carb.:** 20g
Cook: 35 min.   **Prep:** 15 min.

Serves 6

1 tablespoon olive oil

1 onion, diced

2 garlic cloves, finely chopped

2 carrots, diced

2 celery stalks, diced

1 red bell pepper, seeded and diced

1 pound frozen corn

¾ teaspoon salt

½ teaspoon chili powder

4 cups gluten-free vegetable stock

8 ounces silken tofu, drained

2 tablespoons chopped cilantro, to garnish

3 scallions, thinly sliced, to garnish

1 Heat the oil in a large skillet over medium–high heat. Add the onion and garlic and cook for about 5 minutes, stirring occasionally, or until soft. Add the carrots, celery, bell pepper, corn, salt, chili powder, and stock. Bring to a boil, reduce the heat to medium–low, and simmer, uncovered, for about 20 minutes, or until the vegetables are soft.

2 In a blender or food processor, puree the tofu with a ladleful of the soup. Stir the puree into the soup and simmer for about 5 minutes, or until heated through. Serve hot, garnished with the cilantro and scallions.

turkey & cranberry burgers

Calories: 247   **Fat:** 3.5g   **Sat. Fat:** 0.6g   **Salt:** 0.7g   **Carb.:** 69g
Cook: 35 min.   **Prep:** 40 min.

Serves 4

12 ounces lean ground turkey

1 onion, finely chopped

1 tablespoon chopped fresh sage

⅓ cup dry white bread crumbs

¼ cup cranberry sauce

1 egg white, lightly beaten

2 teaspoons sunflower oil, for brushing

salt and pepper

to serve

4 toasted whole-wheat burger buns

½ lettuce, shredded

4 tomatoes, sliced

4 teaspoons cranberry sauce

1 Mix together the turkey, onion, sage, seasoning, bread crumbs, and cranberry sauce in a large bowl, then bind with egg white.

2 Shape into four 4-inch patties, about ¾ inch thick. Chill the patties in the refrigerator for 30 minutes.

3 Preheat the broiler to medium and line the broiler rack with parchment paper, making sure the ends are secured underneath the rack to ensure they don't catch fire. Place the burgers on top and brush lightly with oil. Put under the preheated broiler and cook for 10 minutes. Turn the burgers over and brush again with oil. Cook for another 12–15 minutes, or until cooked through.

4 Fill the burger buns with lettuce, tomato, and a burger, and top with cranberry sauce.

Chapter 4
Desserts & Snacks

mini pumpkin cheesecakes

Vegetarian

Calories: 290   **Fat:** 13g   **Sat. Fat:** 7g   **Salt:** 0.9g   **Carb.:** 39g
Cook: 50 min.   **Prep:** 15 min. plus chilling

Makes 6

Crust

2 sprays of vegetable oil spray

1 cup graham cracker crumbs

2 tablespoons brown sugar

pinch of salt

1 tablespoon unsalted butter, melted

Filling

½ cup reduced-fat cream cheese

½ cup reduced-fat sour cream

1 cup unsweetened pumpkin puree

½ cup sugar

1 large egg

2 egg whites

½ teaspoon ground cinnamon

¼ teaspoon each ground ginger
and ground nutmeg

2 teaspoons vanilla extract

pinch of salt

1 Preheat the oven to 375°F. To make the crust, spray six ½-cup ramekins (individual ceramic dishes) with vegetable oil spray. Pulse the graham cracker crumbs, sugar, and salt in a food processor several times. Add the butter and pulse until well combined. Press the mixture into the bottoms and about halfway up the sides of the prepared ramekins. Bake in the preheated oven for 10 minutes, until beginning to brown. Remove from oven and let cool slightly. Reduce the oven temperature to 325°F.

2 To make the filling, beat the cream cheese, sour cream, pumpkin puree, and sugar in a large bowl until smooth. Add the egg and egg whites and continue to beat until well mixed. Add the cinnamon, ginger, nutmeg, vanilla extract, and salt and beat well.

3 Spoon the filling into the prepared crusts and bake in the preheated oven for about 35–40 minutes, or until the cheesecakes are fully set in the middle. Remove and let cool to room temperature. Cover and refrigerate for at least 4 hours. Run a knife around the edge of each cheesecake to remove it from the ramekin and serve.

apple-berry crisp

Vegetarian

Calories: 237   **Fat:** 7g   **Sat. Fat:** 4g   **Salt:** 0.4g   **Carb.:** 34g
Cook: 45 min.   **Prep:** 10 min.

Serves 8

1 spray of vegetable oil spray

6 Pippin apples, peeled, cored, and sliced

½ cup dried cranberries or dried cherries

¼ cup sugar

½ teaspoon vanilla extract

Topping

½ cup flour

½ cup firmly packed brown sugar

½ teaspoon ground cinnamon

pinch of salt

4 tablespoons butter, at room temperature

½ cup rolled oats

1 Preheat the oven to 375°F. Spray a baking dish with vegetable oil spray.

2 To make the filling, put the apples, dried fruit, sugar, and vanilla extract into a medium bowl and toss to mix thoroughly. Spread the mixture in the prepared baking dish, overlapping the apples a little as necessary.

3 To make the topping, combine the flour, brown sugar, cinnamon, and salt in the bowl of a food processor or in a large mixing bowl. In the processor, or using a pastry cutter or two knives, cut the butter into the flour mixture until it resembles coarse bread crumbs. Stir in the oats.

4 Sprinkle the topping evenly over the filling and bake in the preheated oven for about 45 minutes, or until the topping is crisp and beginning to brown. Serve immediately.

chocolate soufflés

Vegetarian

Calories: 228   **Fat:** 10g   **Sat. Fat:** 6g   **Salt:** 0.4g   **Carb.:** 29g
Cook: 25 min.   **Prep:** 15 min.

Makes 6

2 sprays of vegetable oil spray

2 tablespoons unsalted butter

3 ounces semisweet chocolate, finely chopped

½ cup skim milk

¼ cup unsweetened cocoa powder

1 tablespoon all-purpose flour

1 teaspoon vanilla extract

pinch of salt

4 egg whites

½ cup sugar

1 Preheat the oven to 375°F. Spray six ¾-cup ramekins (individual ceramic dishes) with vegetable oil spray. Put the butter, chocolate, and ¼ cup of the milk in a small bowl and microwave on high for 30 seconds. Stir until the chocolate is melted. Add the cocoa powder, flour, vanilla extract, and salt and beat until well mixed. Add the remaining milk and stir to combine.

2 In a large bowl, beat the egg whites with an electric mixer on high speed for about 3 minutes, or until stiff peaks form. Add the sugar, a little at a time, and continue to beat for about another 2 minutes, or until the mixture is thick and glossy.

3 Gently fold a large dollop of the egg mixture into the chocolate mixture and stir to combine using a rubber spatula. Gently fold the chocolate mixture into the remaining egg mixture until well combined.

4 Carefully spoon the mixture into the prepared ramekins and bake in the preheated oven for about 22–25 minutes, or until the soufflés are puffy and dry on the top. Serve immediately.

pear & blueberry strudel

Vegetarian

Calories: 255 **Fat:** 10g **Sat. Fat:** 4g **Salt:** 0.4g **Carb.:** 67g
Cook: 40 min. **Prep:** 20 min.

Serves 4

2 tablespoons butter

3 Bosc pears, cored and chopped

1 cup blueberries

1 tablespoon light brown sugar

¼ teaspoon ground cinnamon

1 slice whole-wheat bread, toasted and torn into pieces

1½ tablespoons canola oil or sunflower oil

4 sheets of phyllo dough

confectioners' sugar, for sprinkling

low-fat custard or low-fat Greek-style yogurt, to serve

1 Melt 1 tablespoon of the butter in a nonstick skillet. Add the pears and cook over low heat for 5 minutes, or until tender. Transfer to a bowl and let cool. Gently stir in the blueberries, sugar, and ¼ teaspoon of ground cinnamon.

2 Preheat the oven to 350°F. Place the toast and the remaining cinnamon in a food processor and blend to coarse crumbs. Melt the remaining butter with the oil.

3 Lay one sheet of phyllo dough on a clean work surface and brush lightly with the butter mixture (keep the remaining dough covered with a damp dish towel while you work to prevent it from drying). Sprinkle with one-third of the crumbs. Repeat twice more, then cover with the remaining dough and brush lightly with the butter mixture.

4 Spoon the pear mixture along one long edge and roll up. Press the ends together to seal and transfer to a baking sheet. Brush with the remaining butter mixture and bake in the preheated oven for 40 minutes, or until crisp. Sprinkle with a little confectioners' sugar. Serve warm with custard or yogurt.

lemon meringue cookies

Vegetarian

Calories: 73   **Fat:** 0g   **Sat. Fat:** 0g   **Salt:** 0.3g   **Carb.:** 18g

Cook: 2 hr.   **Prep:** 10 min.

Serves 8

2 large egg whites

⅛ teaspoon cream of tartar

pinch of salt

⅔ cup sugar

finely grated zest of 1 lemon

1 Preheat the oven to 200°F. Line a large baking sheet with aluminum foil or parchment paper.

2 In a medium bowl, beat the egg whites with an electric mixer on high speed until they are frothy. Add the cream of tartar and salt and continue to beat on high until soft peaks form. Gradually add the sugar and continue to beat on high for about 3–4 minutes, or until stiff peaks form. Fold in the lemon zest.

3 Drop the batter in rounded teaspoons onto the prepared baking sheet. Bake in the preheated oven for about 1½ hours, or until dry and crisp but not yet beginning to brown. Turn off the oven and let the cookies sit inside for another 30 minutes. Serve at room temperature.

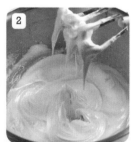

buttermilk brownies

Vegetarian

Calories: 254   **Fat:** 11g   **Sat. Fat:** 6g   **Salt:** 0.3g   **Carb.:** 38g
Cook: 35 min.   **Prep:** 10 min.

Makes 8

1 spray of vegetable oil spray

2 ounces unsweetened chocolate, coarsely chopped

4 tablespoons unsalted butter, cut into pieces

1 cup sugar

⅓ cup unsweetened cocoa powder

½ cup all-purpose flour

¼ teaspoon salt

2 large eggs

½ cup low-fat buttermilk

½ teaspoon vanilla extract

1 Preheat the oven to 350°F. Spray an 8 x 8-inch baking pan with vegetable oil spray.

2 In a microwave-safe dish, combine the chopped chocolate and the butter and heat on high in the microwave for 1 minute. Stir until the chocolate is melted.

3 In a medium bowl, combine the sugar, cocoa powder, flour, and salt. In a large bowl, beat the eggs, buttermilk, vanilla, and the chocolate-butter mixture until well combined. Add the dry ingredients to the wet ingredients and mix well.

4 Pour the batter into the prepared baking pan and bake in the preheated oven for about 35 minutes, or until the top is dry and a toothpick inserted into the center comes out clean. Cool in the pan on a wire rack. Cut into bars and serve warm or at room temperature.

whole-wheat muffins

Stay Fuller For Longer

Vegetarian

Calories: 173   **Fat:** 4.5g   **Sat. Fat:** 0.7g   **Salt:** 0.5g   **Carb.:** 30g
Cook: 25–30 min.   **Prep:** 15 min.

Makes 10

1¾ cups whole-wheat flour

2 teaspoons baking powder

2 tablespoons light brown sugar

¾ cup finely chopped dried apricots

1 banana, mashed with 1 tablespoon
orange juice

1 teaspoon finely grated orange rind

1¼ cups skim milk

1 egg, beaten

3 tablespoons canola oil or sunflower oil

2 tablespoons rolled oats

fruit spread, honey, or maple syrup, to serve

1 Preheat the oven to 400°F. Place 10 muffin cups in a muffin pan. Sift the flour and baking powder into a mixing bowl, adding any husks that remain in the strainer. Stir in the sugar and chopped apricots.

2 Make a well in the center of the dry ingredients and add the banana, orange rind, milk, beaten egg, and oil. Mix together well to form a thick batter. Divide the batter evenly among the 10 muffin cups.

3 Sprinkle each muffin with a few rolled oats and bake in the preheated oven for 25–30 minutes, or until well risen and firm to the touch. Transfer the muffins to a wire rack to cool slightly. Serve the muffins warm with a little fruit spread, honey, or maple syrup.

sweet potato fries

Calories: 202   **Fat:** 1.5g   **Sat. Fat:** 0.5g   **Salt:** 0.7g   **Carb.:** 48g

Cook: 15–20 min.   **Prep:** 10 min.

Serves 4

2 sprays of vegetable oil spray

6 orange-fleshed sweet potatoes (about 2 pounds)

½ teaspoon salt

½ teaspoon ground cumin

½ teaspoon cayenne pepper

1 Preheat the oven to 450°F. Spray a large baking sheet with vegetable oil spray.

2 Peel the sweet potatoes and slice into ¼-inch thick spears about 3 inches long. Spread the sweet potatoes on the prepared baking sheet and spray them with vegetable oil spray.

3 In a small bowl, combine the salt, cumin, and cayenne. Sprinkle the spice mixture evenly over the sweet potatoes, and then toss them with a spatula to coat.

4 Spread the sweet potatoes out into a single layer and bake in the preheated oven for about 15–20 minutes, or until cooked through and lightly browned. Serve hot.

maple-nut granola bars

Vegan

Calories: 200   **Fat:** 10g   **Sat. Fat:** 1.5g   **Salt:** 0.2g   **Carb.:** 14.5g
Cook: 5–7 min.   **Prep:** 15 min. plus chilling

Makes 12

1 spray of vegetable oil spray

1¼ cups rolled oats

½ cup chopped pecans

½ cup slivered almonds

½ cup maple syrup

¼ cup light brown sugar

⅓ cup creamy peanut butter

1 teaspoon vanilla extract

¼ teaspoon salt

1 cup puffed rice cereal

½ cup ground flaxseed

1 Preheat the oven to 350°F. Coat a 9 x 13-inch baking pan with vegetable oil spray.

2 On a large, rimmed baking sheet, combine the oats, pecans, and almonds and toast in the preheated oven for 5 to 7 minutes, or until lightly browned.

3 Meanwhile, combine the maple syrup, brown sugar, and peanut butter in a small saucepan and bring to a boil over medium heat. Cook, stirring, for about 4–5 minutes, or until the mixture thickens slightly. Stir in vanilla extract and salt.

4 When the oats and nuts are toasted, place them in a mixing bowl and add the rice cereal and flaxseed. Add the syrup mixture to the oat mixture and stir to combine. Spread the syrup-oat mixture into the prepared baking pan and chill for at least 1 hour before cutting into 12 bars. Store in a tightly covered container at room temperature. Serve at room temperature.

caramel popcorn bites

Vegetarian

Calories: 230   **Fat:** 7.5g   **Sat. Fat:** 2.5g   **Salt:** 1.3g   **Carb.:** 44g
Cook: 5 min.   **Prep:** 1 hour

Serves 8

½ cup sugar

½ cup light brown sugar

½ cup light corn syrup

2 tablespoons butter

1½ teaspoons baking soda

1 teaspoon salt

½ teaspoon vanilla extract

8 cups plain, air-popped popcorn

1 Cover a large baking sheet with parchment paper or aluminum foil.

2 In a saucepan, combine the sugars, corn syrup, and butter and bring to a boil over medium–high heat. Reduce the heat to medium and boil, without stirring, for 4 minutes. Carefully stir in the baking soda, salt, and vanilla extract.

3 Put the popcorn in a large mixing bowl. Pour the caramel over the popcorn and stir to coat. Using two spoons, form the mixture into 24 balls, about 2 inches in diameter, and place them on the lined baking sheet. Let sit at room temperature for about 1 hour, or until firm. Serve at room temperature.

peanut butter cookies

Vegetarian

Quick & Easy

Calories: 274   **Fat:** 15g   **Sat. Fat:** 6.5g   **Salt:** 0.37g   **Carb.:** 26.5g
Cook: 14–16 min.   **Prep:** 10 min.

Serves 12

1 stick unsalted butter, softened

¾ cup light brown sugar

¾ cup reduced-fat peanut butter
(creamy or crunchy)

1 large egg

1 teaspoon vanilla extract

½ cup rolled oats

½ cup all-purpose flour

½ cup whole-wheat flour

2 tablespoons ground flaxseed

1 teaspoon baking powder

1 teaspoon baking soda

½ teaspoon salt

1 Preheat the oven to 350°F.

2 In a large bowl, cream the butter and sugar with an electric mixer until smooth. Add the peanut butter, egg, and vanilla extract and beat well.

3 In a medium bowl, combine the oats, flours, flaxseed, baking powder, baking soda, and salt. Add the dry ingredients to the wet ingredients and mix well.

4 Drop the batter in rounded tablespoons onto an ungreased cookie sheet and flatten slightly with a fork. Bake in the preheated oven for 14–16 minutes, or until lightly browned on the bottom and around the edges. Let cool on the sheet for a few minutes, then transfer to a wire rack to cool completely. Serve warm or at room temperature.

banana split sundae

Vegetarian

Calories: 296 **Fat:** 10g **Sat. Fat:** 4.5g **Salt:** 0.3g **Carb.:** 49g
Cook: 5 min. **Prep:** 3 hours

Serves 2

2 small bananas

2 teaspoons slivered almonds, toasted

Chocolate sauce

3 tablespoons light brown sugar

3 tablespoons unsweetened cocoa powder

⅓ cup low-fat milk

1 ounce chopped bittersweet or semisweet chocolate

½ teaspoon vanilla extract

1 Peel and dice the bananas, then freeze the diced bananas for 2 hours. In a blender or food processor, process the frozen bananas until creamy. Return the banana puree to the freezer and chill for about 1 hour, or until firm.

2 To make the chocolate sauce, put the sugar, cocoa powder, and milk in a small saucepan and heat to a simmer over medium heat. Reduce the heat to low and cook, stirring continuously, for about 1 minute, or until the sugar and cocoa powder are dissolved. Remove from the heat and stir in the chopped chocolate until it melts. Stir in the vanilla extract. Let the sauce cool slightly.

3 Scoop the banana puree into two bowls, drizzle warm chocolate sauce over the top, and sprinkle with the almonds.

healthy hot chocolate

Vegetarian

Quick & Easy

Calories: 260   **Fat:** 4g   **Sat. Fat:** 2g   **Salt:** 0.6g   **Carb.:** 48g
Cook: 3 min.   **Prep:** 1 min.

Serves 1

1 tablespoon sugar

2 tablespoons unsweetened cocoa powder

pinch of ground cinnamon (optional)

1 cup skim milk

¼ teaspoon vanilla extract

1 large marshmallow

1 In a small saucepan, combine the sugar, cocoa powder, cinnamon (if using), and about 2 tablespoons of the milk. Stir to make a paste.

2 Add the remaining milk and heat to a simmer over medium heat. Cook, stirring occasionally, about 3 minutes, until the cocoa and sugar are completely dissolved.

3 Stir in vanilla extract and serve immediately, topped with a marshmallow.

apples
  Apple-Berry Crisp 120
  Apple Spice Oatmeal 24
avocado
  Fish Tacos with Avocado Salsa 86
  Turkey-Avocado & BLT Wrap 78

bacon
  Spaghetti with Bacon-Tomato
    Sauce 94
bananas
  Banana Split Sundae 140
  Berry Sunrise Smoothie 32
  Chocolate Banana Smoothie 36
Berry Rhubarb Muffins 30
Berry Sunrise Smoothie 32
blueberries
  Blueberry & Honey Yogurt 28
  Pear & Blueberry Strudel 124
Body Mass Index (BMI) 8
Breakfast Burrito 40
Broccoli Pizza 102
Buttermilk Brownies 128
butternut squash
  Butternut Squash & Lentil Stew 88
  Squash & Couscous Salad 58

Caramel Popcorn Bites 136
cheese
  Cheesy Corn Muffins 48
  Chicken Cobb Salad 54
  Crustless Corn & Cheddar
    Quiche 42
  Ham & Cheese Scones 50
  Mini Pumpkin Cheesecakes 118
  Roasted Vegetable Melts 76
  Tomato & Feta Salad 56
Cherry Almond Granola 26
chicken
  Chicken & Spicy Peanut Salad 62
  Chicken & Sun-dried Tomato
    Pasta 106
  Chicken & Vegetable Enchiladas 104
  Chicken Cobb Salad 54
  Chicken Noodle Soup 68
  Chicken Tacos 70
  White Chicken Chili 92
Chipotle-Lime Shrimp Burgers 98
chocolate
  Banana Split Sundae 140
  Chocolate Banana Smoothie 36
  Chocolate Soufflés 122
  Healthy Hot Chocolate 142
cooking methods 19
corn
  Cheesy Corn Muffins 48
  Crustless Corn & Cheddar
    Quiche 42
  Spicy Corn Chowder 112
couscous
  Squash & Couscous Salad 58
Crab Cakes 100
Crab Salad Sandwiches 80
cranberries
  Apple-Berry Crisp 120
  Turkey & Cranberry Burgers 114

eggplant
  Stuffed Eggplant 72
eggs
  Chicken Cobb Salad 54
  Crustless Corn & Cheddar
    Quiche 42
  Egg White Omelet 44
  Poached Eggs in Tomato Sauce 46
exercise 14–15
  calories burned 15

Falafel Pita Pockets 74
fats 13, 18–19
Fish Tacos with Avocado Salsa 86
flavorings 18
food diaries 10–11
food shopping 16–17

ginger
  Roasted Pork with Gingered
    Apples 96
  Green Salad with Yogurt Dressing 82

Halibut with Romesco Sauce 108
Ham & Cheese Scones 50
healthy diet 12–13, 16–17
Healthy Hot Chocolate 142
honey
  Blueberry & Honey Yogurt 28

Lemon Meringue Cookies 126
lentils
  Butternut Squash & Lentil Stew 88
lettuce
  Turkey-Avocado & BLT Wrap 78
lime
  Chipotle-Lime Shrimp Burgers 98
low-calorie diet 6–7, 9

Maple-Nut Granola Bars 134
mindful eating 10
Mini Pumpkin Cheesecakes 118
mushrooms
  Whole-Wheat Crepes 38

noodles
  Chicken Noodle Soup 68
  Sweet & Sour Noodles 90
nutrition labels 13
nuts
  Cherry Almond Granola 26
  Chicken & Spicy Peanut Salad 62
  Maple-Nut Granola Bars 134
  Pumpkin Pecan Pancakes 34

oats
  Apple-Berry Crisp 120
  Apple Spice Oatmeal 24
  Cherry Almond Granola 26
  Maple-Nut Granola Bars 134

pasta
  Chicken & Sun-Dried Tomato
    Pasta 106
  Spaghetti with Bacon-Tomato
    Sauce 94

Peanut Butter Cookies 138
Pear & Blueberry Strudel 124
pita
  Falafel Pita Pockets 74
  Poached Eggs in Tomato Sauce 46
popcorn
  Caramel Popcorn Bites 136
pork
  Roasted Pork with Gingered
    Apples 96
portion size 10
pumpkin
  Mini Pumpkin Cheesecakes 118
  Pumpkin Pecan Pancakes 34

rhubarb
  Berry Rhubarb Muffins 30
Roasted Tomato Soup 66
Roasted Vegetable Melts 76
Romesco Sauce 108

sausage
  Shrimp & Sausage Jambalaya 110
shrimp
  Chipotle-Lime Shrimp Burgers 98
  Shrimp & Sausage Jambalaya 110
  Shrimp Taco Salad 60
Spaghetti with Bacon-Tomato Sauce 94
spices
  Apple Spice Oatmeal 24
  Chicken & Spicy Peanut Salad 62
  Spicy Corn Chowder 112
Squash & Couscous Salad 58
Sweet & Sour Noodles 90
Sweet Potato Fries 132
Sweet Potato Soup 64

tomatoes
  Chicken & Sun-dried Tomato
    Pasta 106
  Poached Eggs in Tomato Sauce 46
  Roasted Tomato Soup 66
  Spaghetti with Bacon-Tomato
    Sauce 94
  Tomato & Feta Salad 56
  Turkey-Avocado & BLT Wrap 78
tortillas
  Breakfast Burrito 40
  Chicken & Vegetable Enchiladas 104
  Chicken Tacos 70
  Fish Tacos with Avocado Salsa 86
  Shrimp Taco Salad 60
turkey
  Chicken Cobb Salad 54
  Turkey & Cranberry Burgers 114
  Turkey-Avocado & BLT Wrap 78
Tzatziki Sauce 74

vegetables
  Chicken & Vegetable Enchiladas 104
  Roasted Vegetable Melts 76

weight loss 6, 7, 8–9
  ideal weight 8
whole grains 13
  Whole-Wheat Crepes 38
  Whole-Wheat Muffins 130

yogurt
  Blueberry & Honey Yogurt 28
  Green Salad with Yogurt Dressing 82